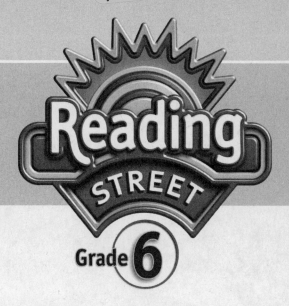

Reading STREET

Grade 6

Scott Foresman

Fresh Reads
for Differentiated Test Practice

Teacher's Manual

PEARSON
Scott Foresman

Editorial Offices: Glenview, Illinois • Parsippany, New Jersey • New York, New York
Sales Offices: Needham, Massachusetts • Duluth, Georgia • Glenview, Illinois
Coppell, Texas • Sacramento, California • Mesa, Arizona

ISBN: 0-328-16988-9

3 4 5 6 7 8 9 10 V031 14 13 12 11 10 09 08 07 06

Contents

NOTES TO THE TEACHER

Introduction

Fresh Reads for Differentiated Test Practice is designed to provide differentiated practice in reading comprehension skills and to prepare students to take the Reading/Language Arts section of standardized tests, state tests, or teacher-made tests. The student book includes the weekly differentiated practice tests to strengthen comprehension skills taught in *Scott Foresman Reading Street.* This Teacher's Manual includes the following: (1) notes on how to use the Fresh Read tests, (2) instructions on how to administer and score a fluency test, (3) a chart on which you may record the progress of your students, and (4) annotated copies of all of the Fresh Read tests indicating the correct answer to all questions.

How to Use the Fresh Read Tests

The purpose of the Fresh Read tests is to give weekly differentiated practice in target comprehension skills taught in *Scott Foresman Reading Street.*

This book contains three Fresh Read tests for each week to be used independently from the main selection in *Scott Foresman Reading Street.* The tests consist of a "Fresh Read" leveled passage and related comprehension items that focus on the target and review comprehension skills of the week but are written to address varying levels of proficiency—Strategic Intervention (SI), On-Level (OL), and Advanced (A). A code at the bottom of each page tells you the level of each test.

You can assess student's proficiency levels using their responses to discussion questions in class and their work on the comprehension pages in the Practice Book or Teacher's Resource Book. Fresh Read tests can be done independently, or you may choose to work through them with students in small groups, in order to give support and assess student's progress.

Other ways to use the Fresh Read test pages:

- use the Strategic Intervention pages for whole-class practice with the comprehension skills and/or test-taking skills

- use the Strategic Intervention pages after introducing the target and review comprehension skills but prior to reading the main selection in the student anthology of *Scott Foresman Reading Street* to assess students' readiness to read that selection

- use the On-Level pages as an assessment tool to check students' understanding of the comprehension skills and/or test-taking skills

- use the On-Level pages to check students' need for further practice, reteaching, or more challenging materials

- use the Advanced pages as a substitute for the comprehension pages in the Practice Book or Teacher's Resource Book for students working above grade level

- use any of the pages as preparation for the unit Benchmark Test

How to Administer and Score a Fluency Test

A fluency test measures a student's reading rate, or the number of words correctly read per minute (wcpm), on grade-level text the student has not seen before. You may want to use a copy of one of the "On-Level" leveled passages from the Fresh Read tests for this purpose. Make a photocopy for yourself of the passage you will give the student. (The pages in this Teacher's Manual have a scale of running numbers to make it easier for you to know how many words the student read during the fluency check, while the passages in the student edition do not have the numbers.) Make sure you have put the student's name and the test date at the top of your copy of the passage. Have a watch or clock with a second hand available for timing the reading.

Give the student a copy of the passage for the test. Note: The student should NOT have seen the passage beforehand; it is a "fresh" reading passage for the student. Do NOT allow the student to read the passage silently before oral reading.

Have the student read the text aloud. Do not have the student read the title as part of the fluency reading; it is not included in the running word count. (You may want to tape-record the student's reading for later evaluation.) Stop the student at exactly one minute and note precisely where the student stopped.

As the student reads orally, on your copy of the text mark any miscues or errors the student makes during the reading (see the chart on page viii). Count the total number of words the student read in one minute. Subtract any words the student read incorrectly. Record the words correct per minute score on the test.

The formula is: Total # of words read – # of errors = words correct per minute (wcpm).

You will likely want to keep the test in your folder for the student. You may also want to record students' progress on the Reading Fluency Progress Chart on page xi.

How to Identify Reading Miscues/Errors

Using the passage on page ix, the chart below shows the kinds of miscues and errors to look for as a student reads aloud and the notations to use to mark them.

Reading Miscue	Notations
Omission The student omits words or word parts.	Anjelo ⟨had⟩ visited his cousin in Connecticut the summer before.
Substitution The student substitutes words or parts of words for the words in the text.	As they approached Sells, Michael could see ~~the~~ *a* beautiful green dome on the Pima County courthouse.
Insertion The student inserts words or parts of words that are not in the text.	Sells wasn't as big or as hot as Michael *had* ⋀ expected.
Mispronunciation/Misreading The student pronounces or reads a word incorrectly.	Anjelo knew what Michael expected *accepted* when he came to Arizona.
Hesitation The student hesitates over a word and the teacher provides the word.	So on the ride from the Tuscon airport toward Sells, the capital of the Tohoro O'odham Nation near the Mexican border, Michael gaped at the huge saguaro cacti they passed.
Self-correction The student reads a word incorrectly but then corrects the error.	"It's not the biggest Indian reservation in Arizona."

Notes

- If the student hesitates over a word, wait several seconds before telling the student what the word is.

- If a student makes the same error more than once, count it as only one error.

- Self-correction is not counted as an actual error. However, writing "SC" over the word or words will help you identify words that give the student some difficulty.

Sample Fluency Test

Here is the passage marked as shown on the previous page. This is the "On-Level" passage from Grade 6, Unit 1, Week 1. As the student reads the passage aloud to you, mark miscues and errors. Have the student read for exactly one minute, and then mark the last word the student reads.

Old Yeller

Name *Susan*   9/4/2009   (122)

Anjelo's Nation

Anjelo knew what Michael expected [*accepted*] when he came to Arizona. Anjelo (had)	12
visited his cousin in Connecticut the summer before, and Michael kept insisting that	25
Arizona was all a flat, dry desert. So on the ride from the Tucson airport toward	41
Sells, the capital of the Tohoro O'odham [*H*] Nation near the Mexican border, Michael	54
gaped at the huge saguaro cacti they passed.	62
"Nation," Michael had mumbled the first time he heard the name. "It must really	76
be a small one."	80
"It's not the biggest Indian reservation [*sc*] in Arizona," Anjelo agreed, noting that it	93
was, however, about the size of Connecticut.	100
As they approached Sells, Michael could see ~~the~~ [*a*] beautiful green dome on the	113
Pima County courthouse. Sells wasn't as big or as hot as Michael [*had*] expected. Anjelo /	127
explained that they were more than two thousand feet above sea level and that it	142
seldom got hotter than eighty degrees there in the summer. Still, Michael couldn't	155
resist suggesting that they stop and buy some bottled water just in case they ran out.	171

127 - 5 = 122

Total number of words read	**127**
number of errors	**– 5**
Words correct per minute	**122**

Interpreting the Results

According to published norms for oral reading fluency, students at the end of Grade 6 should be reading fluently at 150 words correct per minute in text that is on grade level. This chart gives recommended progress toward that goal.

End of Unit/Grade		Reading Rate (wcpm)
Grade 6	Unit 1	115 to 120
Grade 6	Unit 2	120 to 126
Grade 6	Unit 3	125 to 132
Grade 6	Unit 4	130 to 138
Grade 6	Unit 5	135 to 144
Grade 6	Unit 6	140 to 150
End of Year Goal		150

If a student's reading rate is lower than the suggested progress toward the standard for his or her grade level, your notes on the student's miscues may help you determine why the rate is low. Does the student make errors that indicate his or her decoding skills are poor? If so, further instruction in phonics may be needed. Do the errors reflect a lack of comprehension or limited vocabulary? In that case, instruction in comprehension strategies and exposure to more vocabulary words may help. A lack of fluency may indicate a lack of exposure to models of fluent oral reading. It may also mean that the student isn't reading enough material at his or her reading level. "Matching Students to Texts" in the Additional Resources section at the back of the *Scott Foresman Reading Street* Teacher's Editions gives suggestions on increasing reading fluency.

© Pearson Education 6

Reading Fluency Progress Chart

Student's Name	Unit 1		Unit 2		Unit 3		Unit 4		Unit 5		Unit 6	
	Date	WCPM	Date	WCPM	Date	WCPM	Date	WCPM	Date	WCPM	Date	WCPM
1.												
2.												
3.												
4.												
5.												
6.												
7.												
8.												
9.												
10.												
11.												
12.												
13.												
14.												
15.												
16.												
17.												
18.												
19.												
20.												
21.												
22.												
23.												
24.												
25.												
26.												
27.												
28.												
29.												
30.												
31.												
32.												
33.												
34.												
35.												

Reading Fluency Progress Chart

Read the selection. Then answer the questions that follow.

Grandma's Dollhouse

Brandi asked Sandra to accompany her on a visit to Grandma Thisler's house.	13
"She's a wonderful little lady," Brandi said. "I'm just not comfortable in her	26
house."	27
They walked through a fancy wooden gate and up a winding narrow path. "Her	41
house looks like a miniature cottage in a fairy tale!" Sandra whispered.	53
Inside, the girls sat in very small chairs covered with doilies. Plants in tiny pots	68
covered little tables. Brandi seemed nervous and sat with her shoulders up almost	81
around her ears, but Sandra was delighted.	88
Grandma Thisler served hot chocolate, and they chatted about the relatives in tiny	101
pictures all around the small room.	107
Later, when the girls got up to depart, a doily stuck to Sandra's arm. She turned	123
to pick it off, and her elbow knocked a plant off a table.	136
"Whew!" Sandra said outside.	140
"I thought you loved the place," Brandi teased.	148
"I felt like a clumsy doll!" Sandra said.	156

Turn the page.

© Pearson Education 6

Answer the questions below.

1 Which of the following statements best describes Grandma Thisler's place?

   A It is filled with magical things.

   B It is large and fancy like a palace.

   Ⓒ It is small and crowded inside.

   D It is ugly and nearly empty.

2 What did Sandra think of Grandma Thisler's house when she first arrived there?

   Ⓕ She loved it and thought it was wonderful.

   G She was uncomfortable and worried.

   H She could not believe it was real.

   J She wished she could live there.

3 What probably changed Sandra's feeling about Grandma Thisler's house?

   A Grandma Thisler served bitter tasting hot chocolate.

   B Grandma Thisler wanted them not to stay long.

   C Sandra saw how uncomfortable Brandi was there.

   Ⓓ Sandra accidentally knocked a plant off of a little table.

4 Explain what characteristics of Grandma Thisler's house made Sandra feel like "a clumsy doll."

Answers may vary. Possible response: Grandma Thisler's house is small like a dollhouse and full of frames, plants, and things you might break if you aren't very careful. Sandra felt like a doll in a dollhouse.

Read the selection. Then answer the questions that follow.

Anjelo's Nation

Anjelo knew what Michael expected when he came to Arizona. Anjelo had	12
visited his cousin in Connecticut the summer before, and Michael kept insisting that	25
Arizona was all a flat, dry desert. So on the ride from the Tucson airport toward	41
Sells, the capital of the Tohoro O'odham Nation near the Mexican border, Michael	54
gaped at the huge saguaro cacti they passed.	62

"Nation," Michael had mumbled the first time he heard the name. "It must really	76
be a small one."	80

"It's not the biggest Indian reservation in Arizona," Anjelo agreed, noting that it	93
was, however, about the size of Connecticut.	100

As they approached Sells, Michael could see the beautiful green dome on the	113
Pima County courthouse. Sells wasn't as big or as hot as Michael expected. Anjelo	127
explained that they were more than two thousand feet above sea level and that it	142
seldom got hotter than eighty degrees there in the summer. Still, Michael couldn't	155
resist suggesting that they stop and buy some bottled water just in case they ran out.	171

"No shortage of water here," Anjelo said, laughing. "It rains a lot in the summer,	186
and our deep wells fill up. Travelers stop here just to taste the delicious water."	201

Anjelo outlined the agenda for the weeks Michael was to be there. They would	215
go to the desert museum, its zoo, and the botanical garden in Tucson. Another day	230
they would see more than 250 historic planes in the air and space museum there.	245
Anjelo anticipated that the best time would be the camping trip they would take	259
high into the nearby mountains, where there were waterfalls splashing in the crisp,	272
refreshing air.	274

Michael's vacation would be full of surprises.	281

Turn the page.

Answer the questions below.

1 Anjelo's cousin Michael thinks that Arizona is

 A bigger than Connecticut.

 (B) nothing but desert.

 C very mountainous.

 D cold in the summer.

2 From the brief description in this story, which of these would be the best way to describe the area where Anjelo lives in Arizona?

 (F) a varied landscape

 G high in the mountains

 H wet, lush, and green

 J a barren landscape

3 What can Michael expect on his vacation?

 A He will be stuck in a small town far from nowhere.

 (B) He will see and do many interesting things.

 C There will be little to do to pass the time.

 D The heat will make him very uncomfortable.

4 What is the water situation in Sells?

 F People have to survive on bottled water.

 G The place is often flooded.

 (H) They have all the good drinking water they need.

 J Their water is pumped in from Tucson.

5 Why was Michael surprised?

Arizona was not as hot and dry as he had expected.

Read the selection. Then answer the questions that follow.

They Still Can Fly

Great Uncle Fred saw in the newspaper that airplanes like those he had flown in	15
World War II would be at the airport, and he wanted someone to go with him to see	33
them.	34
"Big jets, huh?" I said.	39
"We didn't have jets in those days, Andy," Uncle Fred said, laughing. "These are	53
a B17 and a B24."	58
Our airport has one paved runway and a small cement block terminal. Otherwise,	71
it looks a lot like an empty, unplanted field. Uncle Fred followed other cars around	86
a fence to park on the grass.	93
We saw the planes on display to one side of the runway, and I was amazed at	110
how small they were. They weren't sleek and modern, the way I expected war	124
airplanes to be. They looked boxy, awkward, and kind of ugly.	135
People crowded around them, staring up at names of their crews painted on their	149
sides. We peered into the small glass turrets on their bellies and tails, where men	164
squeezed in beside machine guns. We climbed a rickety metal ladder into the barrel	178
of each plane and walked very carefully from the tail to the cockpit, squeezing past	193
empty bays where bombs were carried.	199
The tight interiors of the planes were bare metal pieces bolted together, with	212
openings in the sides and floors. I wondered how cold and frightening it must have	227
been for the crew and tried to imagine Uncle Fred as a young pilot.	241
We were very quiet coming back to town. We stopped at a grocery, and when we	257
came out, a strange vibrating noise filled the sky. Flying overhead was the rickety	271
old B17 that I had been lucky enough to see up close.	283

© Pearson Education 6

Turn the page.

Answer the questions below.

1 Most of this story takes place

   A outside of a grocery store.

   B inside an airport terminal.

   C in a new jet airplane.

   (D) around and in old airplanes.

2 Which is the best phrase to describe the airport?

   F sleek and modern

   G boxy and awkward

   (H) empty and unused

   J cold and frightening

3 What did Andy notice most about the planes' insides?

   (A) They seemed small and crowded.

   B They looked very modern.

   C There were names written on them.

   D They were very long and roomy.

4 What did seeing the planes make Andy think about?

Andy thought about what it was like for Uncle Fred as a pilot.

5 The next day Andy told a friend that the crew of a B17 must have been really brave men. What did he most likely say about the B17 to help his friend understand?

Flying in the sky in such a cramped and small airplane must have been frightening.

- -

Name _____

Mother Fletcher's Gift

Read the selection. Then answer the questions that follow.

For the Fun of It

The neighborhood children played soccer that summer on an empty, grassy field.	12
The competition began by choosing up teams, and Matthew hated that. He was fast,	26
but his big feet wouldn't change directions easily. Matthew never anticipated being	38
chosen first, but Katie always picked him early in the selection process. She was a	53
terrific soccer player and scored lots of goals.	61
"How come you always choose me?" Matthew asked her. "My big clown feet	74
won't help us win."	78
"Because it's fun to have you on our team," Katie said.	89
The players used huge cardboard boxes for their goals. One day Matthew's dad	102
drove up with goals made of plastic pipe and big netting. Everyone thanked him	116
joyfully.	117
"It was Matthew's idea," Matthew's father said. "He figured out how we could	130
make them."	132
Katie looked at Matthew with a proud smile.	140

© Pearson Education 6

Fresh Reads Unit 1 Week 2 SI

Answer the questions below.

1 Why did Matthew dislike choosing sides for soccer teams?

   A He knew that Katie would expect him to win the game.

   B He thought choosing teams was a waste of time.

   (C) He felt as if he was not good enough to be chosen early.

   D He did not believe Katie really wanted him on her team.

2 What is most likely Katie's main reason for playing soccer?

   (F) to have fun with her friends

   G to show off her soccer talent

   H to have Matthew on her team

   J to help Matthew learn to play better

3 Which of the following is a fact?

   (A) Soccer games began by choosing teams.

   B Katie did not care about winning.

   C Matthew's feet were clown-sized.

   D Matthew was fun to have on a team.

4 What new information about Matthew did you learn in the next to last paragraph?

Answers may vary. Possible response: Matthew likes soccer enough to work on improving his team's game.

Read the selection. Then answer the questions that follow.

The Backpack Litter

Arthur, the librarian, didn't deliberately acquire cats. He couldn't say no to a	13
homeless critter and had ended up with eleven feline roommates. Even strangers	25
seemed to know about Arthur's affinity for cats.	33
One spring day, a college girl plunked her backpack on Arthur's desk and slowly	47
reached in it to lift out a sleepy white kitten. She kept dipping into her bag, and	64
eventually she was shuffling four frisky kittens to keep them all on top of Arthur's	79
desk. None seemed any the worse for the ride in the backpack.	91
The student explained that the kittens had been born four weeks before and	104
needed a home. Arthur's mouth formed the words, "Oh, no!"	114
"I'm leaving town," the young woman said. "I can take their mother home	127
with me, but not the litter. If you won't rescue them, they're destined to go to the	144
shelter."	145
Arthur's cat family was very upset about the newcomers, so he called Maggie,	158
a friend who had lost a cat after twenty years. He insisted that she come and adopt	175
just one kitten.	178
Reluctantly, Maggie picked up an orange kitten. When she turned to leave with	191
it, a black and white one was perching on her foot, clinging to her pants leg. "OK,"	208
she said, "I'll adopt these two."	214
When she got to the door, Maggie looked back at the round black kitten and the	230
tiny white one, sadly watching their remaining family depart. They seemed to be	243
saying, "Wait, what's going on here?"	249
"All right!" Maggie said, sighing and grimacing at Arthur. "I'll take all four and	263
keep them together."	266

Turn the page.

Answer the questions below.

1 Which of the following best describes how Arthur feels about cats?

  A needy

  B suspicious

  C protective *(circled)*

  D uninformed

2 Which is the best word to describe the student in this selection?

  F cold-hearted

  G fun-loving

  H careless

  J responsible *(circled)*

3 Which of the following from the selection is a statement of opinion?

  A Even strangers seemed to know about Arthur's affinity for cats.

  B None seemed any the worse for the ride in the backpack. *(circled)*

  C The kittens had been born four weeks before and needed a home.

  D If you won't rescue them, they're destined to go to the shelter.

4 When the student told Arthur that the kittens would go to the shelter if he didn't take them, she was most likely

  F trying to persuade him to take them. *(circled)*

  G suggesting that the shelter might be a better place for kittens.

  H hoping to impress Arthur with her ability to take care of cats.

  J thinking that would scare the kittens into behaving.

5 Compare Maggie and Arthur. Are they alike or different? Tell how.

They are alike in that they both love cats and feel sorry for them when they need a home. They are different in that Arthur has eleven cats while Maggie, who once had only one cat, now has four.

Name _____

Read the selection. Then answer the questions that follow.

Who's Critical Now?

"Davie needs to calm down considerably," Felix announced at lunch, as if it were | 14

an absolute fact. "He's a real comedian, but sometimes he embarrasses me by being | 28

too silly and upsetting adults." | 33

"Juanita has lots of relatives in Mexico," he went on. "But we'd never know that | 48

because she doesn't seem to know anything about Mexico." Juanita shrugged in | 60

agreement when he added, "She didn't even know about Cinco de Mayo. I had to | 75

tell her what it was and why lots of people celebrate it." | 87

An Yang and Felix were close friends, but she didn't escape his judgment. "An | 101

Yang is way too positive in the way that she never criticizes her friends. She ought | 117

to let us know what she likes about us and recommend ways we could improve." | 132

An Yang responded immediately to Felix's suggestion that she should let her | 144

friends know what was wrong with them. "The trouble with you, Felix," she said, | 158

"is that no one ever has to guess what you think. You can't talk about people—or | 175

anything for that matter—without revealing exactly what you think." | 185

"He's too mouthy, is what he is," Davie contributed. "He has interesting | 197

comments about people and other stuff, but I get really tired of it eventually." | 211

"Well, his continual judgment hurts my feelings sometimes," Juanita said, "and | 222

anyway, he's not always perfectly right about everything." | 230

"Ahem!" Felix grunted, looking at his friends with a serious face. "I was going | 244

to admit that you guys are not as opinionated as I am, but you just made that really | 262

difficult." | 263

Turn the page.

Answer the questions below.

1 Which character appears most sensitive to criticism?

    A Davie

    (B) Juanita

    C An Yang

    D Felix

2 Which of the following is a fact, not an opinion?

    F Davie needs to calm down.

    (G) An Yang and Felix are close friends.

    H An Yang ought to tell her friends what she likes about them.

    J Felix is not always perfectly right about everything.

3 Which of the following best describes Felix?

    A protective

    B unconcerned

    C cautious

    (D) talkative

4 Describe each character's reactions to Felix's criticisms.

An Yang responds by telling Felix that everyone knows he speaks his mind. Davie says that he gets tired of Felix's talking. Juanita admits that she's hurt by the criticisms.

5 Do any of the characters in the selection appear to undergo a permanent change because of their conversation? Explain why or why not.

No character has a permanent change. Possible response: An Yang is critical of Felix, but she does not seem likely to be critical of him again, and she is not critical of anyone else. Felix jokes at the end, so he is not likely to stop being critical.

Read the selection. Then answer the questions that follow.

First Things First

They called themselves "The Young Yanks," and they were on their way home	13
from Yankee Stadium after a baseball game in the last month of the season.	27
On the subway, Tao decided to play a game to pass the time. "If you had your	44
choice between a weeklong vacation in a rustic cabin in the Pocono Mountains and	58
one on the beach at Atlantic City, which would you pick?"	69
"That's easy," Keith said. "I'd pick the mountains, even if it just meant living out	84
in a tent. I'd want good fishing and some canoeing too."	95
Tao groaned.	97
"Oh, man," Shing said, "I'd love to stroll the boardwalk in Atlantic City for a	112
week, and relax in the sun and splash around in the water."	124
They all looked at Claudio, waiting for his choice. "I'd stay right here, guys," he	139
said, giving Tao a thumbs up. "The baseball playoffs are coming up soon for the	154
pennant. My team needs me right here."	161

Turn the page.

Answer the questions below.

1 **Which of the boys would most likely be considered an outdoorsman?**
- **(A)** Keith
- **B** Shing
- **C** Claudio
- **D** Tao

2 **Which boy appears to dislike camping out?**
- **F** Keith
- **G** Shing
- **H** Claudio
- **(J)** Tao

3 **What activity probably appeals most to Shing?**
- **A** camping in a tent
- **B** fishing in the ocean
- **(C)** going swimming
- **D** watching baseball

4 **How do you know that Claudio is a serious baseball fan?**

He won't even consider a vacation while baseball is still being played.

Read the selection. Then answer the questions that follow.

An Important Decision

When the Martinez family moved to the big city, Yoli had a very important	14
decision to make. She would have the choice of attending Jefferson Public School	27
(Number 27) or Kendleton Middle School.	33
Jefferson was an old structure in a suburb just across a river that ran through	48
downtown, and it served the area where Yoli's family lived. Jefferson had long halls	62
that echoed the voices of its students, but it was built of warm brown brick, and Yoli	79
thought it had a friendly-looking entrance.	85
Kendleton was both old and new. It was part of a plan the city had initiated	101
within its school system to buy unusual buildings and turn them into newly	114
designed schools. There was a high school on a couple of floors of a big office	130
building, for example, and Kendleton had been created in an abandoned factory. It	143
was near downtown, and everything in it was new and very sleek and modern.	157
Yoli visited both schools and had lunch in their cafeterias. The students and	170
teachers at both schools seemed very friendly. At Kendleton, there was an attractive	183
gymnasium that also served as an auditorium, but at Jefferson, the principal, Mrs.	196
Abbingez, asked Yoli a lot of questions about Yoli's life and family. She took the	211
time to find out what kinds of activities interested Yoli.	221
When it came time to choose, Yoli's parents expected her to select Kendleton	234
because it was so new and interesting, but Yoli kept thinking about Mrs. Abbingez	248
and picked Jefferson.	251

© Pearson Education 6

Turn the page.

- -

Answer the questions below.

1   Compared to Kendleton, Jefferson Middle School was

    A   boldly modern in structure.

    (B)   an old-fashioned brick school.

    C   designed as an office building.

    D   old and in need of many repairs.

2   What part of her new school's building helped Yoli make up her mind?

    F   its halls

    G   the cafeteria

    H   the gymnasium

    (J)   its entrance

3   What does Jefferson have that Kendleton may not have?

    A   friendly students

    B   a cafeteria

    (C)   an interested principal

    D   a high school very nearby

4   What does Yoli's decision tell us about her?

    (F)   People are more important to her than buildings.

    G   Modern buildings are not attractive to her.

    H   She likes to visit new and different places.

    J   She does not like noise or crowds.

5   How are the Kendleton and Jefferson school buildings alike?

Jefferson is an old building, and Kendleton is built in an old factory building.

© Pearson Education 6

Read the selection. Then answer the questions that follow.

Playing the Game

The sixth graders at Eastview Middle School played *Scrabble*® when Mrs.	11
Martin introduced the game in class. They used wooden tiles with letters on them	25
to form words. They placed the tiles on the game boards she had brought.	39

They consulted dictionaries to find words to make with some of the seven letters	53
each player had drawn, and classmates who observed were encouraged to assist the	66
players. Edmundo and Christa maintained a list on the chalkboard of all the words	80
being created.	82

After the initial play, an additional word had to connect to some word already on	97
the board. Tony liked to keep the board "open" with lots of places for interesting	113
words to cross or touch other words. He often played his words near pink and blue	129
squares that doubled or tripled the points of letters or whole words. Tony hoped his	144
opponents could play on those and earn big scores too.	154

Chuck tried to place letters on those colored squares himself, being careful not to	168
create opportunities for other players. His objective was to score more points than	181
his opponents. He even reread the rules and announced that using dictionaries was	194
not allowed.	196

Chuck discovered that clever *Scrabble* players can bluff by creating words	207
that aren't really words. Would the made-up word *stigits*, for example, lead his	220
opponents to challenge it or to worry about losing a turn if it really was a word?	237

Mrs. Martin praised Tony's approach, but Chuck was the one who got his	250
classmates to learn the actual rules and to compete during the activity period.	263
By the next year, members of the Eastview *Scrabble* Team were competing in	276
tournaments. Chuck won one and his picture appeared in the local newspaper.	288

SCRABBLE is a registered trademark of Hasbro, Incorporated.

Turn the page.

© Pearson Education 6

Answer the questions below.

1 Who wanted to play the game the way it is meant to be played?

   A Mrs. Martin

   B Tony

   C Christa

   (D) Chuck

2 Who was probably responsible for starting the Eastview Scrabble Team?

   F Tony

   G Christa

   (H) Chuck

   J a newspaper reporter

3 Compared to Tony's approach, Chuck's approach to playing the game made Chuck

   A less likely to win.

   B more considerate of other players.

   C less interested in words.

   (D) more competitive.

4 What excited Tony most about playing Scrabble?

Answers may vary. Possible response: Tony would get excited about seeing the words everyone would form.

5 Why was Tony's approach to Scrabble probably more pleasing to Mrs. Martin than Chuck's approach was?

Answers may vary. Possible responses: Tony's approach makes learning new words while having fun more important than winning. Chuck's way makes winning the most important thing.

© Pearson Education 6

Read the selection. Then answer the questions that follow.

It Can Be Nice to Dream

The Nutcracker ballet is a beloved holiday tradition. In it, young Clara dreams	13
that her toys come alive. A nutcracker shaped like a soldier, a gift from her	28
godfather, leads toy soldiers into battle. Clara has to save the nutcracker from the	42
evil mouse king and his army.	48
Soon the nutcracker becomes a prince. He and Clara dance with snowflakes in	61
the Land of Snow. Then they meet the sugar plum fairy in the Land of Sweets.	77
Very creative productions of this ballet have been designed around the world for	90
more than one hundred years. At our Bijou Theater last night, a huge screen (really	105
a frame), was hung at the rear of the stage. In the frame behind her, Clara's dreams	122
came to life while she stood dreaming in front of it. Gradually, the characters from	137
her dreams appeared onstage to wake her to dance and, near the end of the scene, a	154
sleeping Clara (played by another actress) was alone in the frame.	165
This clever staging showed how our dreams can live beside our realities. It was	179
nice to be reminded!	183

The Bijou Theater Ballet
December 18
The Nutcracker
Music by Pyotr Ilyich Tchaikovsky
Based on a book by E.T.A. Hoffman

CAST
Clara, a young girl .... Ema Schisstle
Clara, as she dreams .... Maria Ifflesta
her brother Fritz .... Bobby Fultz
Fritz in the dream .... Anton Barrow
Godfather Drusselmeyer........ Herbert Standose
The Nutcracker........................... Al Hembert
The Prince .... William Atz

Turn the page.

Answer the questions below.

1 Based on the selection, which of the following is a statement of opinion?

(A) The big frame hung at the back of the stage was a good idea.

B *The Nutcracker* ballet has been staged all over the world.

C *The Nutcracker* ballet is based on elements of Clara's dreams.

D Modern versions of old ballets can include creative staging.

2 Which of the following, based on the selection, is a statement of fact?

F Clara's godfather meant for his gift to inspire her to dream.

(G) In her dream, Clara defeats the evil mouse king.

H The author is an expert on and lover of traditional ballets.

J *The Nutcracker* ballet focuses on confusion between fantasy and reality.

3 The music for this ballet was written by

(A) Tchaikovsky.

B Hoffman.

C Schisstle.

D Bijou.

4 There were two actresses playing Clara onstage at the same time. What does this staging suggest?

Answers may vary. Possible responses: It shows how our dreams and realities can exist simultaneously. It can also show how our dreams can become our realities.

Read the selection. Then answer the questions that follow.

The Awesome Backpack

Margaret Kay was shopping for a new backpack when she saw an advertisement	13
for the *Rock-It!* "Wow!" she cried out loud. "That is the coolest backpack I've ever	28
seen!"	29
The *Rock-It!* was long and sleek, with a big flap at the top that opened to a	46
full-length, deep pocket and had a zipper covered by a waterproof fly seal that kept	61
books and papers dry from any rain or snow. Another flap halfway down opened to	76
a hard-case storage pocket, which was actually a lightweight plastic box sewn in to	90
protect more valuable possessions.	94
Stored under that were C batteries that ran two blue lights flashing out of the	109
bottom of the backpack, to look like jets—they were purely for decoration. Between	123
the student and the backpack, there was an attached inflatable comfort pad to	136
cushion the student's back.	140
"What are the lights for?" Margaret Kay's mother asked.	149
"Aren't they the most awesome thing you've ever seen?" Margaret Kay said.	161
"The air-filled pad is sensible," her mother responded; "but there's no pocket for	174
pencils. This just doesn't seem to be a wise purchase. Let's browse at the mall for	190
one with wheels so you can roll it on the pavement when your back gets tired."	206

The *Rock-It!* Backpack

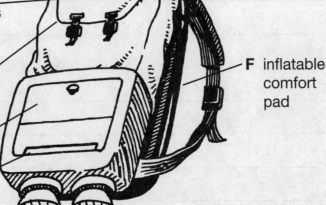

A full-length, deep pocket for books

B waterproof "fly" seal

C hard-case storage pocket

D storage for batteries

E *Rock-It!* lights

F inflatable comfort pad

Turn the page.

Answer the questions below.

1 Which of the following represents a statement of opinion?

   A Margaret Kay saw an advertisement for the *Rock-It!*

   B The backpack had a zipper covered by a waterproof fly seal.

   (C) The *Rock-It!* was better than other backpacks.

   D Two blue lights were purely for decoration.

2 The batteries that run the lights of the *Rock-It!* were stored

   F under the top flap.

   G in the hard-case pocket.

   H under the inflatable comfort pad.

   (J) near the bottom of the backpack.

3 Based on the story, which of the following is a statement of fact?

   A The *Rock-It!* sold very well.

   B Margaret Kay got a backpack with wheels.

   C The *Rock-It!* plastic case for valuables cracked easily.

   (D) Margaret Kay and her mother disagreed about backpacks.

4 Based on information in the story, what is Margaret Kay's mother's opinion of the blue lights?

   F They are a fire hazard.

   (G) They are interesting but useless.

   H Rain might ruin them.

   J After dark, they will work as reflectors.

5 Which feature of the *Rock-It!* backpack is most likely to be helpful to athletes?

The inflatable comfort pad could help someone who has sore muscles or an injury.

Read the selection. Then answer the questions that follow.

Dragging Canoe's Losing Battle

For more than sixty years, the Cherokee suffered from the smallpox epidemic and | 13
from battles with tribes that tried to claim their land in the Carolinas. The Cherokee | 28
have been called warlike because they often fought the French and eventually | 40
turned against their uneasy ally, the British. They felt that a good offense was | 54
essential to keep their land, which stretched west to the Mississippi River. In fact, | 68
Cherokee villages suffered raids by white settlers. | 75

In 1750, twelve-year-old Tsi'ui-Gunsin'ni wanted to join the battle, but no one | 87
believed he was old enough and strong enough to fight. He was challenged to pull | 102
a fully loaded log canoe from the shore into the water. He performed the task and | 118
earned the name Dragging Canoe. Dragging Canoe suspected that the Cherokee | 129
people would ultimately lose most of their land to the American settlers, so he spent | 144
the rest of his life refusing to yield to them or the French. | 157

In 1775, Richard Henderson, a businessman from North Carolina, bought twenty | 168
million acres of land from the Cherokee for a mere two thousand pounds of sterling | 183
and six wagon loads of goods. Dragging Canoe insisted that Henderson was | 195
swindling the Cherokee out of their ancestral hunting grounds. | 204

Although the Henderson deal was made invalid by both the British and American | 217
governments, Dragging Canoe fought on, choosing to side with the British in | 229
the Revolutionary War, not the American settlers. In one battle, he was severely | 242
wounded though he made a recovery. After a final victory, it was said that he | 257
celebrated too much, for he died the next morning at the age of fifty-four. | 271

The Americans won the Revolutionary War against the British, and by 1838 | 283
almost all of the Cherokee land had been taken over by the settlers—just as | 298
Dragging Canoe had predicted. | 302

Dragging Canoe was once the leader of Malaqua, a town on an island in the Little Tennessee River. It is now completely flooded by the Tellico Dam.

Turn the page.

© Pearson Education 6

Answer the questions below.

1 Based on the selection, which of the following is a statement of opinion?

   A The Cherokee have been called warlike.

   (B) Henderson cheated the Cherokee out of their lands.

   C Dragging Canoe never gave up fighting to keep Cherokee land.

   D Dragging Canoe was one of the youngest Indian braves to go to battle.

2 Based on information in the selection, which of the following is a statement of fact?

   F The Cherokee would have fared better had they not sided with the British.

   (G) The Cherokee fought aggressively to keep their land.

   H Henderson hoped to obtain Indian land for an unfairly low price.

   J The land Henderson bought was taken over by the British.

3 Which of the following statements supports the opinion that Tsi'ui-Gunsin'ni would make a good warrior?

   (A) Tsi'ui-Gunsin'ni was confident in his abilities to fight in battle.

   B Tsi'ui-Gunsin'ni always dreamed of becoming a warrior.

   C Tsi'ui-Gunsin'ni was not strong enough to fight.

   D Tsi'ui-Gunsin'ni was twelve years old.

4 What does the caption of the picture tell you about Dragging Canoe as a grown man?

He became a leader of his people.

5 What does the Tellico Dam's location suggest about Dragging Canoe's prediction about the future?

Dragging Canoe accurately predicted that the Cherokee would lose their land.

Read the selection. Then answer the questions that follow.

We Need Help!

Dear Editor,	2
Martin Skateboard Park is well worth saving! We need adult volunteers to keep it	16
open.	17
Getting this park took four years of sacrifice. Many of us kids and our parents	32
worked very hard for hundreds of hours. We got approval from the park's board	46
of directors for the space. We raised the money for its construction, and we built it	62
ourselves. Now we need adults to manage the place.	71
The Park Board made us get insurance to cover any accidents. The insurance	84
company insists on having adult supervisors in charge. They know the park can	97
make skateboarding safer. They also want to be sure all skateboarders wear pads	110
and helmets as well as behave in a sensible way.	120
Martin Skateboard Park is truly an awesome place! It has eight ramps that range	134
in levels of difficulty. There are a variety of handrails, ledges, and blocks. It also	149
has a street course to teach off-park skills and safety.	159
We need places to keep kids busy and out of trouble. We must not close this	175
wonderful park!	177
Sincerely,	178
Tabatha Wilson	180

Turn the page.

- -

Answer the questions below.

1 Which of the following is a statement of fact?

   A Martin Skateboard Park is well worth saving.

   (B) Adult volunteers are needed to keep the park open.

   C Completing the park took years of sacrifice.

   D Martin Skateboard Park is an awesome place.

2 Which of the following is a statement of opinion?

   F The Park Board required insurance to cover any accidents.

   G The insurance company insists that adult supervisors be present.

   (H) Martin Skateboard Park is an awesome place.

   J The eight ramps in the park vary in difficulty.

3 Which of the following tells you that Tabatha is a young person who uses the park?

   (A) She uses the phrase "us kids and our parents."

   B She writes a lot about the Park Board.

   C She mentions the insurance company.

   D She signs the letter using her first name.

4 What information in the letter bests supports the claim that "the park can make skateboarding safer"?

Answers may vary. Possible response: The park has a street course that teaches skills and safety. The adult supervision will help make it safe too.

Read the selection. Then answer the questions that follow.

The Wonder of Winter

I got sentimental while Roberto and I were out shoveling a couple of feet of snow | 16

surrounding the family car. I related how, when I was his age, the other boys and | 32

I would build daring slopes along the riverbank. We'd pour water on the slopes to | 47

freeze them. They'd endure for weeks. Today's snow was the heaviest in years, but | 61

it will only last a week or so before it melts away. | 73

While inside, warming up for another go at shoveling, I read some of my favorite | 88

winter poems and writings to Roberto. William Wordsworth wrote a wonderful | 99

poem about his memories ice-skating at Hawkshead. He wrote about skating at | 111

night on the lake near his boyhood school in England. | 121

John Greenleaf Whittier was snowbound in New England. He and his family | 133

tunneled through deep snow to feed some animals. Then they huddled around a fire | 147

as the heavy, silent blanket piled high against their house. | 157

Henry David Thoreau kept a fascinating journal and told about his long, rugged | 170

cross-country skating trips on frozen streams in New England. | 179

Finally, I read Robert Frost's poem about stopping with his horse to watch the | 193

woods fill up with snow. | 198

"I guess we should go finish digging out the car," Roberto said dreamily, staring | 212

out the window. I thought I saw a special light in his eyes. They reflected the old | 229

promise that a new snowfall holds. | 235

Turn the page.

- -

© Pearson Education 6

Answer the questions below.

1 Which of the following is a statement of opinion?

   A The family car was buried under a couple of feet of snow.

   (B) The slopes the main character and his friends built were daring.

   C The main character read some of his favorite descriptions of winter.

   D Wordsworth's memories were from Hawkshead.

2 Which of the following is a statement of fact?

   F Thoreau's exciting journal described a fascinating cross-country skating trip.

   G There was a special light in Roberto's eyes.

   H Today's snow will only last a week or so.

   (J) Whittier and his family tunneled through snow.

3 Why did the main character read to Roberto?

   A to avoid the unpleasant task of digging out the car

   (B) to recall pleasant visions of winter weather

   C to illustrate how boys were braver when he was young

   D to teach Roberto that he should read more poetry

4 The main character's description of how he helped make a slope for sledding when he was a boy supports his opinion that

   F Roberto was not enjoying the snow.

   G winter was getting more severe each year.

   (H) shoveling snow can bring back pleasant memories.

   J only famous writers can appreciate winter.

5 The main character summarizes four writing samples that illustrate winter sentiments. Given the examples, what is the main character's opinion of winter?

Answers may vary. Possible responses: The main character expresses winter as a season full of wonder, instilling the idea in Roberto. The main character has pleasant memories about the season from his own childhood. He has also read a lot about winter.

Read the selection. Then answer the questions that follow.

Still Some Concerns

When the group of parents and children who championed having a public	12
skateboard park began lobbying the City Council to build one, we began to have	26
serious concerns.	28
Sure, a skateboard park seemed to be an interesting idea. Clearly, the city had	42
plenty of space in any one of several city parks. Yet we wanted to weigh the other	59
costs. We praised the Council's questions of caution: How many children would use	72
such a park? Was the cost a wise investment of public money?	84
However, neither the Council nor The Journal Times fully appreciated the	95
community's enthusiasm over the park. The parents and children raised the money	107
needed to cover its construction. Then, perhaps too quickly, the Council approved	119
using space in Martin Park.	124
The problem is that building the park was not the only cost. As we suggested	139
back then, skateboarding is not an accident-free sport. Some studies suggest there	151
are no more accidents in skateboarding than in other sports, but that skateboarding	164
tends to result in more serious injuries. Sliding on a skateboard along hand rails	178
mounted in cement does seem risky. The Council eventually recognized that there	190
were risks for the city. But it was too late. The park was built. The only solution	207
has been getting expensive insurance to cover any lawsuits over accidents. Now the	220
insurance company has insisted on continual adult supervision of activities at the	232
park. They want to avoid accidents.	238
So far, there are not enough adults willing to supervise the place, so the park has	254
not reopened. One wonders what has happened to all the supportive adults who first	268
helped build the park. Why haven't they stepped up to fill this requirement? Maybe	282
the possibility of accidents worries them too.	289

Turn the page.

- -

© Pearson Education 6

Answer the questions below.

1 Which of the following from the selection is a statement of fact?

  A A skateboard park seemed like an interesting idea.

  B The city had plenty of space in any one of several city parks.

  C The kids and their parents raised the money to fund its construction.

  D The Council approved using space in Martin Park too quickly.

2 Which of the following from the selection is a statement of opinion?

  F Sliding along hand rails mounted in cement is risky.

  G The Council recognized that there were risks for the city.

  H The insurance company has insisted on continual adult supervision.

  J There are not enough adults willing to supervise the place.

3 Which detail in the selection supports the statement that building the park was not the only expense?

  A The people who wanted the park raised the money to build it.

  B It was not clear how many kids would use the park.

  C The Council obtained insurance to cover any lawsuits over accidents.

  D Too few adults had volunteered to act as supervisors in the park.

4 What opinion in the selection is supported by the studies about accidents?

Answers may vary. Possible response: Skateboarding can lead not just to accidents but to injuries more serious than those in other sports.

5 What do you think is the author's purpose for writing this selection?

Answers may vary. Possible response: The author's purpose is to air concerns about opening the skateboarding park.

© Pearson Education 6

Fresh Reads   Unit 1 Week 5 A

Read the selection. Then answer the questions that follow.

Ashlee's Second Song

In 2004, on a live TV show, singer Ashlee Simpson began to sing her second	15
song as planned. It turned out to be the same song she had sung earlier that night.	32
Noticing the mistake, she stopped moving her lips. Her voice went right on singing.	46
Someone behind the scenes had put on the wrong recording for Ashlee to lip-	60
synch (move her lips along with the words but not actually sing out loud). Because	75
the show was live, Ashlee was supposed to be singing. Ashlee was embarrassed and	89
ended her performance.	92
Reporters called this Ashlee's "Milli Vanilli Moment." Milli Vanilli was a popular	104
singing group of two young men. In public performances, they lip-synched to the	117
voices of other singers—the singers who had made Milli Vanilli's recordings. When	130
the group was discovered to have been lip-synching all along, their singing careers	143
were over.	145
It doesn't seem fair to ruin Ashlee's career. People have been lip-synching for a	159
long time. Famous movie stars in musicals had to lip-synch if their singing voices	173
were bad. At least Ashlee was lip-synching to a recording of her own voice.	187

Turn the page.

Answer the questions below.

1 The topic of this selection is
- **A** Milli Vanilli.
- **(B)** lip-synching.
- **C** musicals.
- **D** actors who sing.

2 What is the main idea of this selection?
- **F** Ashlee Simpson's career is ruined.
- **G** Ashlee Simpson only recorded one song.
- **(H)** Lip-synching is more common than we think.
- **J** People might prefer to see singers lip-synch.

3 Which generalization can be made from this selection?
- **A** All singers who lip-synch will eventually get caught.
- **B** Most singers lip-synch once in a while.
- **C** No lip-synching should be done on live TV.
- **(D)** All lip-synching should be done to your own voice.

4 Based on the selection, what could happen as a result of lip-synching?

Answers may vary. Possible responses: Lip-synching could ruin a singer's credibility or career. People may not be willing to pay money to attend the concerts of singers who may be lip-synching during their performances.

Read the selection. Then answer the questions that follow.

Familiar Faces

Long before photography became available to the public in 1839, people obtained	12
portraits from painters. Painters usually earned a living doing portraits of family	24
members, royalty, and people who could afford to pay for their own likenesses on	38
canvas.	39
Painters sometimes chose to paint people who were not well-known. In the	51
1600s Jan Vermeer of Delft, Holland, painted women who appeared to be living or	65
working in his house. One such painting is called *Girl with a Pearl Earring*. The	80
model remains a mystery. Art historians do not know who she was. In 1999 a novel	96
based on research and imagined details about this unknown girl, Vermeer, and the	109
painting was published. The novel was so popular it was made into a movie.	123
Another of Vermeer's portraits is called *Girl with a Red Hat*. The girl peers right	138
at the viewer from under a very bright red-orange hat that catches the light on its	154
top. The brim of the hat shadows her eyes so the light strikes just the lower half of	172
her face. Another famous portrait including a hat is Thomas Sully's *The Torn Hat*,	186
a painting made around 1820 of his young son outdoors. The boy's rosy face is lit	202
beneath a large straw hat with a downturned brim. The straw brim is partly torn	217
away from the crown of the hat, letting mellow sunlight fall on just one area of the	234
boy's face. These effects of light and shadow are very pleasing to the eye.	248
Many well-known portraits are now available as framed prints, posters, postcards,	260
and calendars. Most of the subjects were not famous during their time, but the	274
painters who chose them made the faces of their subjects famous and beloved	287
throughout the world.	290

Turn the page.

Answer the questions below.

1 Which of the following is a generalization you can make from this selection?

(A) Many paintings are of people who wanted to see their likenesses on canvas.

B Artists hope their lives will be made into movies.

C Very few famous portraits have been made with figures wearing hats.

D Most famous portraits include someone wearing a hat.

2 Another title for this selection could be

F "Hats in Paintings."

G "The Work of Vermeer."

(H) "Subjects in Art."

J "The Role of Light in Paintings."

3 What is the main idea of this selection?

A Long before photography, people had portraits painted of themselves.

B A novelist writing about Vermeer made up details about his life.

C Famous portraits are usually of someone in the painter's household.

(D) Some portraits are widely reproduced many years after being painted.

4 Which of these would best introduce the third paragraph?

F Thomas Sully was a well-known American portrait painter.

(G) In two famous oil portraits, the subjects are wearing hats.

H Hats spoil the faces of the subjects in some portraits.

J Two examples show how portraits are not as good as photographs.

5 What is the purpose of the hat in *Girl with a Red Hat* and *The Torn Hat*?

Answers may vary. Possible response: The artists used the hats to cast shadows on parts of their subjects' faces, creating a contrast in shade that is pleasing to the eye.

Name _____

Read the selection. Then answer the questions that follow.

Why Is Sue Like a Bird?

No one is suggesting that Sue, the most complete skeleton of a Tyrannosaurus	13
Rex ever unearthed, could fly. Her reconstructed remains at the Field Museum in	26
Chicago are a gigantic forty-two feet long and thirteen feet high at the hip. It is	42
estimated that this dinosaur weighed seven tons!	49
More than two hundred of Sue's bones were uncovered near Faith, South Dakota,	62
in 1990 by fossil hunter Sue Hendrickson. Analysis of the bones indicated that this	76
dinosaur existed near the end of the Cretaceous age about sixty-eight million years	89
ago.	90
Scientists are fascinated by the numerous characteristics about dinosaurs that are	101
similar to those of birds. Sue walked with three toes forward, one toe back, and a	117
claw on each toe, just as most birds do. Like Sue, birds have a neck curved like the	135
letter s and have hollow but strong bones.	143
A distinguishing characteristic of most birds is that they have an unusual	155
wishbone. It is made up of small yet long connected bones running side by side.	170
We aren't sure what a bird's wishbone accomplishes. When some scientists used a	183
special X-ray camera to photograph birds flying in wind tunnels, they learned that	196
the wishbone is stretched wide like a spring when a bird's wings arch downward	210
during flight. It is believed that this helps the bird fill its body with air as it flies. It	229
is not clear, though, what purpose this serves.	237
Sue has a wishbone too. Still, no one has contended that Sue could fly. The	252
similarities between birds and the dinosaur have raised questions. We now wonder	264
how birds today are related to dinosaurs.	271

© Pearson Education 6

Turn the page.

Answer the questions below.

1 The topic of this selection is

A the Field Museum.

B Sue Hendrickson.

C dinosaurs and birds.

D wishbones.

2 Which of the following best expresses the selection's main idea?

F Sue might have been able to fly.

G A dinosaur weighs about seven tons.

H A distinguishing characteristic of most birds is a wishbone.

J There appears to be some relationship between birds and dinosaurs.

3 Which of the following best expresses the main idea of paragraph four?

A Sacs in a bird's body fill with air as it flies.

B The purpose of a bird's wishbone is not clear.

C The wishbone is stretched wide when a bird's wings arch downward.

D An X-ray camera was used to photograph flying birds.

4 What are some details in the selection that directly relate to the main idea?

Answers may vary. Possible responses: Sue had birdlike feet, an _S_-curved neck, and strong, hollow bones.

5 What details in the selection make it clear that Sue was not a bird?

Answers may vary. Possible response: Her weight and size.

Read the selection. Then answer the questions that follow.

The Old Oak Stool

"It was probably made between 1910 and 1925," Cynthia wrote, "but it isn't as	14
plain as 'Mission Oak' usually is, so I'd like to know more about it. It's beautiful."	30
Richard, her cousin, wrote back explaining that before the stool belonged to	42
him, it belonged to Old Tom, their grandfather. Cynthia replied that the stool really	56
ought to belong to her, then, because so many relatives said that she and Grandpa	71
Tom, who shuffled along with his toes pointed outward, both walked like ducks.	84
Whenever Cynthia objected to this comparison, her family said she was cranky too,	97
just like her grandpa.	101
The cousins lived far apart, but they exchanged e-mails regularly. Cynthia kept	113
teasing Richard about wanting the stool, and finally Richard explained how he used	126
to stop by Grandpa Tom's house almost every weekday and polish the old man's	140
shoes while he sat on the stool.	147
"Aha," Cynthia conceded, "no wonder it's with you! I've just been teasing. I have	161
some of Grandpa Tom's antique maps."	167
One day the stool was delivered to Cynthia's house in a large box. In turn, she	183
mailed one of Grandpa Tom's maps to Richard.	191
Cynthia posted this picture of the stool on the Internet.	201

Answer the questions below.

1 Which of these sentences would best open the second paragraph and introduce the selection's main idea?

A Richard and Cynthia had the same grandfather.

B Mission Oak furniture is not always the same.

C⃝ Cynthia wanted the stool from the first time she saw it.

D Cynthia looked a lot like her grandfather, Old Tom.

2 Which of these would make a good last sentence to the third paragraph to summarize its main idea?

F⃝ Richard had fond memories of those times.

G Richard and Cynthia were very good friends.

H Deep down, Cynthia didn't really want the stool.

J Old Tom saw Richard almost every weekday.

3 Which of these comments do you think Cynthia wrote under the picture of the stool when she posted it on the Internet?

A "What is this antique stool worth in today's market?"

B⃝ "Information wanted about this stool."

C "Here's some Mission Oak that may surprise you."

D "Is this a stool or a table?"

4 Based on the story, why did Cynthia send Richard one of Grandpa Tom's old maps?

Cynthia was grateful for the stool, and she sent Richard one of Grandpa Tom's old maps to thank him.

Read the selection. Then answer the questions that follow.

How Has San Marino Managed to Stay Independent?

San Marino, the world's smallest republic, is a mere twenty-seven square miles	12
of the Apennine Mountains, which run like a backbone north and south in Italy. Just	27
a few miles southwest of the resort of Rimini and near the Adriatic Sea, San Marino	43
is nestled on the rugged terrain. Its people live on and around the three peaks of	59
Mount Titano. The mountain is only about twenty-five hundred feet high, yet it	72
looks like a very high, steep fortress. Up in the city of San Marino, more than four	89
thousand residents, and many visiting tourists, look down on the surrounding Italian	101
countryside.	102
Its beginnings are somewhat shrouded in legend, but the history of San Marino	115
shows how it was destined to become a republic. Folklore has it that about A.D.	130
350, two stone workers settled on the rise. These eventual founders of San Marino	144
had been brought to Italy to rebuild a stone wall in Rimini. Having completed the	159
task, they were seeking protection from the locals, who did not welcome strangers.	172
Over the next thousand years, the people who settled there formed the republic. The	186
people chose members of each family to select leaders to rule.	197
For hundreds of years, San Marino has managed to stay uninvolved in many	210
European and worldwide conflicts. This is not because it served as a type of	224
fortress. Instead, the leaders of this tiny republic managed to stay neutral. Today, its	238
27,000 citizens speak Italian and use the Euro for currency. They are, however, still	252
independent of any other state.	257

Turn the page.

Answer the questions below.

1 Which of the following best expresses the main idea of the second paragraph?

   A San Marino's beginnings are somewhat shrouded in legend.

   (B) The history of San Marino shows how it was destined to become a republic.

   C About A.D. 350, two stone workers settled on the rise.

   D The founders of San Marino had been brought to Italy to rebuild a stone wall.

2 Which sentence would best begin and express the main idea of the last paragraph?

   F The steepness of Mount Titano assured the independence of the people.

   G Over the years, the population of San Marino ballooned.

   (H) The leaders of the tiny state decided it was necessary to stay out of disputes.

   J There was growing interest in Europe and Italy, in particular.

3 The picture of San Marino reinforces which key word in the selection?

   A resort

   (B) fortress

   C leaders

   D neutral

4 Which sentence would best begin the selection and express its main idea?

   F The history of any state can predict how large it will become.

   G People who refuse to fight will usually avoid disputes.

   H If you live on a mountain, you can look at the people down in the valley.

   (J) The people of a tiny republic can avoid political conflict.

5 Identify details in the second paragraph that are not directly related to the main idea of the selection.

The details in the second paragraph that are not directly

related to the main idea of the selection have to do with

why the two founders of San Marino were in Rimini.

Read the selection. Then answer the questions that follow.

The Ugli Fruit

It seems possible, but not certain, that the orange took its name from its color. It	16
is certain that the ugli fruit got its name from its appearance. This cross between an	32
early species of grapefruit and the orange is truly ugly. The ugli fruit can vary in	48
size. Its color is best described as a blotchy yellow, green, and orange. It has ugly	64
scars and pock marks, and the puffy bumps that make it easy to peel give it a very	82
distorted appearance.	84
So why would anyone ever taste the unappetizing-looking ugli fruit? This strange	96
fruit has a delicious pinkish-orange flesh with a sweetly tart, citrus flavor. It can be	111
eaten like a tangerine or cut in half like a grapefruit. It is also very tasty in a variety	130
of salads and desserts. Some people feel that its name is unfair and have wanted to	146
pronounce it *oog´-li* (as in *oodles*).	152
The ugli fruit was discovered in Jamaica. It was not grown on purpose but	166
came about by accident. At first it was unique to Jamaica, but by cultivation and	181
marketing, it spread to Florida in the 1930s. It remains somewhat unusual, and	194
there has been a shortage of it as the demand for the fruit has increased. In addition	211
to this the ugli harvesting season is short, lasting only from December into April.	225
This results in prices between two and three dollars each, so enjoying the ugli is not	241
inexpensive.	242

Nutrition Facts about the Ugli

(medium-sized)

Calories	35
Calories from Fat	0
Total Fat	0%
Saturated Fat	0%
Sodium 0 mg	
Carbohydrates 10 g	3%
Fiber 0 g	0%
Protein 1 g	
High in Vitamins A and C	

© Pearson Education 6

Turn the page.

Answer the questions below.

1 Which sentence best states the main idea of this selection?

   A The ugli fruit has an unappetizing appearance.

   B The ugli fruit is a cross between a grapefruit and an orange.

   (C) The ugli fruit may be ugly, but it is tasty.

   D The ugli fruit is costly.

2 Which sentence would be the best opening sentence to state the main idea of the first paragraph?

   F If you ever travel to Jamaica, be sure to try an ugli fruit.

   (G) Looking at the ugli fruit probably won't make you hungry.

   H There is little that is special about the look of an ugli fruit.

   J The ugli fruit has a delicious flavor.

3 Which sentence below, taken from the second paragraph, states its main idea?

   (A) So why would anyone ever taste the unappetizing-looking ugli fruit?

   B This strange fruit has a delicious pinkish-orange flesh with a sweetly tart, citrus flavor.

   C It can be eaten like a tangerine or cut in half like a grapefruit.

   D It is also delicious in a variety of salads and desserts.

4 Since its discovery in Jamaica, has the ugli's popularity increased or decreased? Use details from the selection to support your answer.

Answers may vary. Possible responses: The ugli's popularity has increased. It is now grown in Jamaica and in the United States. There is a shortage because so many people want it.

5 Based on the information in the graphic, would the ugli make a good or bad choice for a breakfast fruit if you were trying to avoid fat and sodium? Explain.

It would be a good choice because it has no fat and no sodium.

Read the selection. Then answer the questions that follow.

A Great Way to Get Around!

We intended to buy ten-gear bicycles. Then we saw the shiny black VeloSolexes | 13

silently zipping around the French port city Le Havre. Way back then, they cost | 27

only $68 each! | 30

With the motor doing the work, we got great views of the beautiful valleys by | 45

sitting up straight with both feet up and having the freedom to rubberneck. The | 59

tiny motors rubbing against the front tires propelled us at an ideal viewing speed of | 74

fifteen miles an hour. Going up hills we assisted the motor by using the pedals. So | 90

we got some of the exercise we had anticipated. | 99

In Paris, thousands of Solexes braved the crazy traffic. Out on the open road, | 113

however, no other Solexes loaded with camping gear were seen. As we traveled the | 127

country on our laden Solexes, the curious French often stopped us with friendly | 140

questions. | 141

The motor on the Solex didn't always run smoothly. Yet my memory of them is | 156

very positive. When I saw an ad the other day that said they are being exported to | 173

the United States, I couldn't resist paying close attention. | 182

The VeloSolex in America!*

First manufactured in France in 1946, this RETRO-styled transportation is back** in 2006! With answers to lots of problems!

- Over 200 miles per gallon of gas! (Tank holds enough for over 60 miles.)
- The quietest, most dependable motor on the streets!
- Uses **unleaded** gasoline!
- For riders of many ages!

Tres chic! (as they say in France) ONLY $1,299

The VeloSolex weighs only 62 pounds. It is not a moped! It is a **power-assisted** bicycle. Millions have been sold in Europe, China, and other places. . . . AND NOW IT IS AVAILABLE IN THE UNITED STATES!

The Reliable "Solex" can go up to 23 mph on the level! Power-assisted on hills.

- One-cylindered, two-stroke engine with a friction wheel on the front tire.
- Front and rear brakes, commanded by hand levers.
- Front and rear lights.
- Specialty items available include heated handlebar cuffs.

*Not a replica, but the <u>original</u> 1946 model with an engine modified to run on unleaded fuel with 2-3% oil! Made with the original VeloSolex manufacturing tools!

Available in all 50 states.

**Sold to a moped manufacturer who stopped its production in 1988. It is now being manufactured again under new ownership.

Turn the page.

Answer the questions below.

1 What detail in the ad appears to be contradicted by the selection?

   A The VeloSolex goes over sixty miles on a tank of gas.

   B The rider must assist the motor on hills.

   (C) The motor is the most dependable on the streets.

   D The motor rubs against the front tire.

2 What detail in the ad supports the story's comment about Solexes that impressed the writer in Le Havre?

   F The Solex uses unleaded gasoline.

   G The Solex has hand-controlled front and rear brakes.

   H Solexes are all designed like the 1946 model.

   (J) The Solex motor is the quietest on the streets.

3 Which comment in the ad refers to the VeloSolex's place of origin?

   A "This RETRO-styled transportation is back in 2006!"

   (B) "*Tres Chic!* (as they say in France)"

   C "The VeloSolex weighs only 62 pounds."

   D "Specialty items available include heated handlebar cuffs."

4 What did the speaker most likely think when he saw today's price for a VeloSolex? Explain.

He must have been shocked. The VeloSolex sells for almost twenty times as much as he paid for the one he bought in France years earlier.

Read the selection. Then answer the questions that follow.

Knowing Your Stars

The constellations are imaginary patterns of stars that help us identify which	12
star is which. For more than six thousand years, people have named the patterns	26
that stars seem to make. Yet those in a particular constellation are usually not	40
close together. Their relationship that makes the pattern depends on their sizes and	53
distances from us and on the angle of our view.	63
Ursa Major, the Big Bear, is shaped something like a bear and is the third-largest	78
of the eighty-eight constellations. Another that actually looks something like its	89
popular name, the Little Dipper, is Ursa Minor. However, its pattern of faint stars is	104
not easy to pick out on a clear night when the sky seems packed with stars.	120
The Big Dipper, on the other hand, is formed by bright stars and can be identified	136
fairly easily. It is a part of Ursa Major and is not officially a constellation, but	152
it helps us locate other stars. The two stars at the end of its bowl are called the	170
pointer stars because an imaginary line drawn between them points up to Polaris,	183
the relatively faint North Star. Polaris marks north more accurately than a magnetic	196
compass, so if you are looking toward it, you are always looking north.	209
Once you locate Polaris, it's easier to find the Little Dipper because Polaris is at	224
the end of its long handle. In between the two dippers, the constellation Draco, the	239
dragon, curves lazily across the sky. Knowing where to look enables you to spot	253
his snakelike body and his	258
large square-shaped head.	261
There are practical values to	266
recognizing constellations,	268
but just identifying them	272
makes the night sky much	277
more interesting.	279

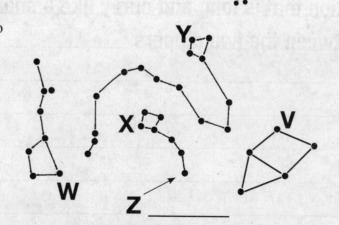

Turn the page.

Answer the questions below.

1 Compared to Ursa Minor, the Big Dipper is
  A fainter and harder to find.
  (B) brighter and easier to find.
  C made up of many more stars.
  D closer to the North Star.

2 Which letter on the diagram represents Ursa Major?
  (F) W
  G X
  H Y
  J Z

3 The Little Dipper is identified on the diagram by which letter?
  A V
  B W
  (C) X
  D Y

4 What name should be written on the chart by the letter Z?
  F Ursa Major
  G Draco
  (H) Polaris
  J The Big Dipper

5 If you were going to substitute the name Draco for one of the letters on the diagram, tell which letter you would replace and why you decided that constellation is Draco.

Draco would go where the letter Y is because that is the

constellation that is long and curvy like a snake and because

it is in between the two dippers.

© Pearson Education 6

Name _____

Read the selection. Answer the questions that follow.

The Theory of Tectonic Plates

Over the last hundred years, there have been interesting explanations of the	12
Earth's geological wonders revolving around a general tectonic plate theory. It	23
states that the Earth's crust consists of a dozen or more plates that ride on a layer of	41
hot, liquid magma. They slide around, striking and pressing against each other and	54
sometimes allowing eruptions of magma. An ocean basin or a continent, or more	67
commonly both, may ride on a single plate.	75
Before 1912, many believed that the earth had once been a molten ball, and as	90
it cooled, its cracking surface created its terrains. However, in 1912, a new theory	104
asserted that the world began as one big continent. It broke apart and drifted in	119
different directions. In 1929, another theory suggested that the continents had	130
moved as if on a kind of conveyor belt. They moved because the earth was always	146
being heated and cooled by the magma escaping from under its crust.	158
By the 1960s, theorists noted that wide, high mountain ridges form on the	171
ocean floor, forcing it to spread out toward the continents while making very deep	185
crevices. This has led to theories about how an ocean plate pressing against a	199
continental plate might slide under it, causing earthquakes.	207
These theories also explain how magma erupts as lava and how heat escaping	220
from the ocean floor's mountains causes the ridges that make the ocean expand. All	234
these ideas are more complex than can be reported in a summary, but it looks like	250
they fit well within a general tectonic plate theory.	259

Ideas that Tend to Fit the "Tectonic Plate" Theory

Date	Theory Name	Theorists	Comments on the Theory
Before 1912	"Contraction"		The Earth, a molten ball, cracked and folded up on itself as it cooled.
1912	"Continental Drift"	Alfred Wegener	One big continent (Pangaea: *all lands*) broke apart and drifted into the positions of the world's continents today. The leading edges of the continents "encountered resistance" and folded upwards, making mountains.
1929	"Thermal Convection"	Arthur Holmes	Based on Wegener's theory, Holmes's theory proposed that repeated heating and cooling caused by escaping magma caused the continents to move.
1960s	"Sea-floor Spreading"	Howard Hess and R. Deitz	Accepting Holmes's theory, new technologies mapped the ocean's floor, where there were growing and heat-emitting ridges. A deep trench runs along the ocean's length, and this region experiences an elevated number of earthquakes and pushes the floor ever farther apart and slowly against the continents.
Since the 1960s	"Subduction"		When sea-floor spreading presses an ocean plate against a continental plate, the heavier rock of the sea plate slides under the continental plate.
Fairly recently	"The Gaia Theory"	James Lovelock	Lovelock's controversial theory builds on the tectonic plate theory proposing that the Earth is one immense, interacting, and dynamic system. One seismic event can have effects anywhere, even a half a world away.

Turn the page.

© Pearson Education 6

Answer the questions below.

1 Which theory was the first to challenge the old theory that the Earth had been a molten ball?

   A the "Contraction" theory

   (B) the "Continental Drift" theory

   C the "Sea-floor Spreading" theory

   D the "Subduction" theory

2 Whose theory focused on the happenings at the bottom of the oceans?

   F Wegener's

   G Holmes's

   (H) Hess and Deitz's

   J Lovelock's

3 Which idea might most directly explain an earthquake in the state of California?

   A "contraction"

   B "continental drift"

   (C) "subduction"

   D "the Gaia theory"

4 Why doesn't a tectonic plate theory contradict Alfred Wegener's theory?

The continents could have drifted because they broke into the tectonic plates.

5 What did Arthur Holmes's theory add to Alfred Wegener's?

It explained what had caused the continents to drift.

Read the selection. Then answer the questions that follow.

Field or Stage?

After practice that day, the coach offered Edmundo the position of starting	12
linebacker. His best friend, Kai, was going to be the quarterback. So if Edmundo	26
decided to play football, he and Kai would be teammates.	36
Making this decision would be tough for Edmundo. West Eicher's drama club	48
was about to start rehearsals for a rap musical called "Why Cinco de Mayo?" about	63
the significance of that holiday. Edmundo loved the feeling he got from performing.	76
He dreamed of becoming many things, but being an actor or singer was at the top.	92
At the same time, he looked for ways to express pride in his Mexican heritage. He	108
had been offered the starring role. The problem was that rehearsals and football	121
practice were scheduled at the same time.	128
"I'm feeling really strong," he told Kai after practice. "Being teammates would	140
be fun."	142
"Performing would also be fun for you," Kai pointed out. "I know deciding will	156
be hard." He gave Edmundo's shoulder a friendly squeeze. "We'll be friends either	169
way."	170

Turn the page.

Answer the questions below.

1 What was Edmundo doing at the beginning of the story?

   A rehearsing for the musical

   B trying out for the musical

   (C) having football practice

   D talking to Kai

2 Edmundo's choice was between getting to be his best friend's teammate or

   F playing the quarterback position.

   G celebrating Cinco de Mayo.

   H working out at football practice.

   (J) singing and acting onstage.

3 Why couldn't Edmundo be on the football team and also be in the musical?

   A The coach demands that players focus on football only.

   (B) Football practice and rehearsals are at the same time.

   C Football might damage his singing voice.

   D Edmundo would not have time to do homework.

4 One of the ways Edmundo could affect people is by helping the team have a winning season. What other way could Edmundo affect people?

Answers may vary. Possible response: He could be in the musical and share his pride in his Mexican heritage with the audience.

Read the selection. Then answer the questions that follow.

A Ride on the Mountaineer

The two-day tour on one of Canada's Rocky Mountaineer trains was one I'll	13
always remember. We boarded at Vancouver in British Columbia on a Tuesday	25
in April. The same day, trains left Banff and Calgary, heading westward toward	38
Vancouver.	39
Like proud parents, the Mountaineer staff do not want passengers to miss any of	53
the view, so the tour proceeds only in daylight. We stopped overnight at Kamloops,	67
halfway along the route. In the morning, we took the part of the train going to Lake	84
Louise and Banff, in Alberta.	89
On the train, the sense of protected comfort inside and the beauty rolling by	103
outside was pleasant. It was like lounging in a little hotel suspended in a cable car.	119
In the bubble observation car, I turned 360 degrees around to see the spectacular	133
view surrounding me, and I felt like a virtual camera. But as we wended our way, I	150
reminded myself that those high sentinels spreading their white capes all around me	163
were real mountains, not travel posters.	169
They were immensely comforting, like silent judges on some very supreme court.	181
Their robes spread downward into the valleys on either side of the track, where	195
a green carpet of firs covered their feet. At the tracks just below us, a somewhat	211
indifferent inspector was checking out the train. A huge moose stood before us as	225
we paused in a pass.	230
Near Banff, we could expect a breathtaking jewel, the emerald Lake Louise. But	243
first, while staying overnight in Kamloops, I stared out my hotel window like a	257
child expecting gifts. I promised myself that I'd take the longer tour next time. Then	272
I could have days to set off into the mountains ("scampering," they call it) expecting	287
to see grizzly bears, eagles, and cougars.	294

© Pearson Education 6

Turn the page.

Answer the questions below.

1 The staff who plan the Mountaineer tours are compared to

(A) proud parents.

B train conductors.

C jewels.

D children.

2 When will the author get to see more wildlife in the Canadian Rockies?

F after he reaches Kamloops

G when he goes tracking for moose

H once he gets film for his camera

(J) on another tour at some later time

3 How does the author feel about all the things to see in that part of Canada?

A like a weary traveler

B like someone's parent

(C) like an excited child

D like an old judge

4 The "indifferent inspector" in this selection is

F an employee of the Mountaineer tours.

G one of the Mountaineer trains.

(H) a huge moose.

J the writer himself.

5 What aspect of the view from the observation car makes the author feel like a virtual camera?

Answers may vary. Possible response: The fact that he can turn all the way around in a circle and that there is always a view makes him feel like a virtual camera.

Name _____

Read the selection. Then answer the questions that follow.

An American Game

Roque is an unusual outdoor game that is not played in many places these days.	15
Like croquet, the object of the game is to use a wooden mallet to hit one or two	33
balls in the correct order through a series of metal hoops called wickets. When the	48
croquet yard game was brought to the United States from England and Ireland in	62
the late 1800s, however, someone changed the game considerably. Someone gave	73
it a new set of rules, a different course, and different equipment. It was so different	89
from croquet that the name was changed too, by dropping the c and the t.	104
Croquet had been played in the Summer Olympics in Paris in 1900, the only time	119
croquet was an Olympic sport. The French won. The Olympics were in St. Louis in	134
1904, and roque was included in those competitions. The three medal winners were	147
all Americans that time.	151
There are distinctive differences between roque and croquet. The roque mallet	162
is shorter and heavier, the balls are made of rubber not wood, and the ten wickets	178
are narrower. Around the outside of a hexagonal course, which has a firm surface	192
instead of the grass used for the rectangular croquet course, there is a short wall	207
often lined with rubber. The game involves *caroming,* or banking, the ball off that	221
wall bumper to angle it at the wickets. So roque is like a cross between croquet and	238
pool or billiards. Many believe roque takes more skill than croquet.	249
Like croquet, roque was a part of only one Summer Olympics, for it did not gain	265
much popularity anywhere. Although roque is still played in the U.S. Midwest,	277
Americans had returned to croquet by the 1920s.	285

Turn the page.

Answer the questions below.

1 In what way are the games croquet and roque alike?

(A) The object of the game is the same.

B They both use similarly sized mallets.

C The width of the wickets are the same.

D The shape of the courses are similar.

2 How are the Olympic histories of the two games alike?

F The competitions were both held in Paris.

G Americans won both the croquet and roque competitions.

(H) Each game was part of only one Olympics.

J The same teams competed in 1900 and 1904.

3 When were the rules for roque created?

A before croquet became popular in England and Ireland

(B) after croquet had come to America

C before croquet came to America

D sometime after the 1920s

4 What requirement would make roque more difficult to set up in a typical backyard than croquet?

Roque requires a rubber wall to carom the balls off.

5 Explain why and how it is believed we got the name *roque* for the game.

The new rules made the game different from croquet. The
name of the game was changed because Roque was different
enough from croquet. The letters c and t were dropped to form
roque.

Read the selection. Then answer the questions that follow.

A Snack at Brunches

The softball team's bus broke down in Almstead, halfway to Middletown. The	12
driver knew a man there who could help repair it within an hour.	25
That meant the game would start late. "I'm hungry!" Thelma griped. "I'll never	38
make it through five innings!"	43
So Coach Eller and his wife led them to an elegant cafe called Brunches. The	58
only other customers were six silver-haired ladies.	65
"Weird menu!" Thelma groaned. "There aren't any lunches listed."	74
"I'll treat everyone to a snack," Coach Eller said.	83
"I'll pick something then," Thelma said. "OK, I love cucumbers!"	93
"Thelma," Claudia said, giggling, "those aren't really cucumbers you ordered."	103
"The menu says cucumbers," Thelma insisted.	109
"THEY'RE SLUGS!" Marilyn shrieked, after Claudia whispered in her ear.	119
"They're called 'sea cucumbers,' " Mrs. Eller said. "But they're actually sea	131
slugs. They're a delicacy in some countries," she added.	140
Thelma's stomach knotted.	143
Mrs. Eller said, "I ordered chicken salad, and I'll swap with you, Thelma."	156
Thelma sighed gratefully.	159

Brunches			
Breakfast Menu		**Munchies**	
Choice of cereal with whole milk & bananas	$1.00	Fried green tomatoes	$1.25
		Sea cucumbers	2.95
Stack o' whole-wheat cakes with maple syrup and butter	$1.75	Turkey bacon	1.50
		Celery sticks	.40
Bowl of fresh fruit of the day with milk or cream	$1.50	**Drinks**	
		Milk	.60
Grilled cheese with (cheddar or Swiss on whole wheat bread)	$2.75	Orange juice	.60
		Hot chocolate	.80

© Pearson Education 6

Turn the page.

Answer the questions below.

1 Why does Claudia say that the menu is not for lunch?

(A) The restaurant's menu says "Breakfast Menu".

B The menu lists turkey bacon as a "munchie."

C No one would eat celery sticks for lunch.

D It is too early for the team to eat lunch.

2 Other than the sea cucumbers, what is the most expensive item on the menu?

F Fried green tomatoes

G Turkey bacon

(H) Grilled cheese sandwich

J Whole-wheat cakes

3 Claudia had a bowl of fresh fruit. What did it cost?

A $1.00

(B) $1.50

C $1.25

D $1.75

4 Do you think Thelma's snack will probably satisfy her until she can get back home from the game? Why or why not?

Answers may vary. Possible response: I think Thelma's snack will keep her from getting hungry until she gets home because it was a sandwich, and sandwiches can be filling.

© Pearson Education 6

Read the selection. Then answer the questions that follow.

Ricardo on the Defensive

The Ramirez Middle School basketball team was having a perfect year. They	12
were nine games into the schedule, and had been victorious in every game. Ricardo	26
was very satisfied with their performance. "It's a super season!" he said.	38
"How can you claim that?" Mickey said. "Our offense gets punier every time we	52
compete. If we keep this up, by the end of the season we'll be scoring zero!"	68
"We scored over fifty in only one game!" Jolon protested.	78
"There's more to basketball than the offense," Ricardo said.	87
"The last time I checked," Mickey said, "the object of the game was to get the	103
ball through the hoop. You don't get points if you don't do that."	116
"We scored more points than our opponents every time out," Ricardo said,	128
wanting to explain, not boast. "What's more important," he added, "is that with one	142
exception, each opponent got fewer points than the last team we played."	154
Ricardo was disappointed that his teammates didn't understand his main point,	165
so he made a graph to illustrate it. He showed it to Mickey and Jolon. "Look at	182
the lines on the graph," he said. "They show that we're successful because we're	196
continually improving our defense!"	200
"Well, the offense should also be improving," Jolon said, "so why isn't it?"	213
"Well, every team we play seems to be playing better defense than the previous	227
team on the schedule," Ricardo said. "I think we've started something."	238

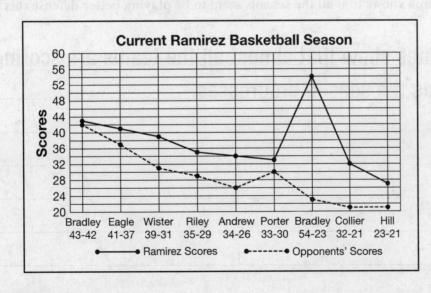

Current Ramirez Basketball Season

Turn the page.

Answer the questions below.

1 Which team has Ramirez Middle School played twice this season?
- (A) Bradley
- B Wister
- C Riley
- D Porter

2 Which part of Ricardo's line graph makes the main point he wanted to make?
- F The line for the Ramirez scores generally keeps going down.
- G Ramirez scored more than fifty points in one of the games.
- (H) The line for the scores of their opponents generally keeps going down.
- J The scores were very close in several of the games.

3 What would it take for the graph to show what Mickey wants to see?
- A The line for the opponents' scores would have to be much higher.
- (B) The line for the Ramirez scores would have to go up, not down.
- C The line for the opponents' scores would have to be much lower.
- D One or two teams would need to outscore Ramirez.

4 Which of the following is the main difference between the two lines on the graph?
- (F) One line represents Ramirez, and the other line is for eight different schools.
- G One line is for the current season, and the other line is for all the past seasons.
- H One line shows all games Ramirez has played and the other line does not.
- J Only one of the lines is in sequential order.

5 What part of the graph shows that all the schools seem to be playing better defense this season?

The scoring lines show that almost all the teams are scoring fewer points as the season progresses.

Read the selection. Then answer the questions that follow.

The Birthday Gift

For his birthday, Harold got a computer desk that came with five separate panels, | 14

a bag of screws, and instructions for assembly. | 22

The Simplex Quick-Space Computer Desk 5-14—Assembly Instructions | 30

The desk comes partially assembled, and finishing it is a simple task of four easy | 45

steps: | 46

1. Identify the five panels with the letters A–E temporarily affixed to them and | 61

   the pouch of fourteen screws—six 2-inch screws and eight $1\frac{3}{4}$-inch screws | 73

   and a hex wrench. | 77

2. Insert the six longer screws into the predrilled holes using the hex wrench to | 92

   attach sides (Panels B and C) to the back (Panel A). **Be sure the dark side** | 108

   of each panel faces inward. The metal rails already attached to Panels B | 121

   and C should be inside and closer to the top. Note that these three panels go | 137

   together to allow space behind the desk to hide cords. | 147

3. Insert the eight shorter screws into the predrilled holes to attach the computer | 161

   shelf (Panel D) to the desk. Two of these screws go through Panel A from | 176

   the back of the desk. The shelf will sit between the two rows of oblong holes | 192

   precut in Panel A that accommodate thick electrical cords. An extra pair of | 205

   hands is helpful to complete this step. | 212

4. Slide in the keyboard and mouse shelf (Panel E) with the metal wheel | 226

   assembly already attached. It snaps into the metal rails on Panel B and Panel | 240

   C about three inches below Panel D. It should roll easily inward and outward. | 254

Now place your monitor | 258

and printer on top of your | 264

desk and your computer on | 269

the floor underneath your | 273

desktop. Now you are **ready** | 278

to compute! | 280

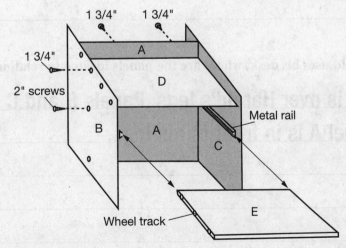

1 3/4"   1 3/4"

1 3/4"

2" screws

A

D

B   A   C

Metal rail

Wheel track

E

Turn the page.

Answer the questions below.

1 Why do you think the manufacturer put the numbers "5-14" into the name of the desk?

   A to suggest it should only take five hours and fourteen minutes to put it together

   B to show it is just a number that attracts a buyer's attention

   (C) to indicate that the desk consists of five panels and fourteen screws

   D to distinguish the desk the company makes from the other four models

2 The metal parts already attached to some of the panels should be

   (F) fitted together when the shelf is added.

   G on the outside of the desk.

   H near the bottom of the desk.

   J removed before finishing the desk.

3 What does this computer desk not have?

   A a shelf for the monitor

   B holes to run the cords through

   (C) a special shelf for the computer itself

   D room to hide the wires behind it

4 Looking at the diagram, explain how the fit of the sides (Panels B and C) to the back (Panel A) will allow space to hide computer cords.

When the side panels are screwed onto the back panel, the overlapping creates space between the back of the desk and the wall behind it. The cords are then hidden in that space.

5 When Harold uses his desk, where are the panels located in relation to his legs?

Panel D is over Harold's legs. Panels B and C are on the sides and Panel A is in front of his legs.

Read the selection. Then answer the questions that follow.

How Those Things Work

The Wingarts' garage was full of everyday things made mysterious by dust. One	13
June when the Wingart twins were twelve years old, they went rummaging through	26
some of it.	29
"Let's construct a time machine!" Anton suggested.	36
Herb agreed as he uncovered a motorless riding mower.	45
"We'll travel forward and reveal the rest of the summer," Anton said. "Or should	59
we drift back to last summer?"	65
"We can go a lot farther than that," Herb said.	75
They used cardboard boxes, tape, and old wallpaper rolls. The machine looked	87
scientific in the dark of the garage, but it wouldn't leap time, no matter how many	103
magic words they uttered. Still, they sat and predicted what would happen that	116
summer. . . .	120

*   *   *

Through with college and home for one last summer, the Wingart twins	132
discovered the time machine still sitting in the garage. They laughed hard at it, and	147
then Anton climbed aboard and made a noise like a jet motor.	159
"Remember the great times we had back then?" he said.	169
"Yes," Herb said, taking a seat on the riding mower. They spent an hour recalling	184
that summer, being twelve, and all the adventures they'd had.	194
"You know," Anton said, "this machine works after all. It took us back ten	208
years!"	209

Turn the page.

Answer the questions below.

1 What does the row of asterisks in the middle of this story represent?

  A that the time machine is about to work

  (B) that years have passed

  C that the twins are thinking really hard

  D that time has drifted backward

2 When does the end of the story actually take place?

  F the same summer in which the story begins

  G the summer before the one in which the story begins

  H next summer, a year after the summer in which the story begins

  (J) ten years after the summer in which the story begins

3 The climax of this story is when

  A the twins discover the old riding mower.

  B the time machine doesn't work.

  C the twins discover the machine is still in the garage.

  (D) one twin remarks that the machine worked after all.

4 Explain what Anton meant when he said the time machine worked.

  The time machine worked because it brought back many
  memories of the summer in which they built it.

_____

_____

_____

_____

_____

_____

_____

Read the selection. Then answer the questions that follow.

Pale Male and Lola

In December of 2004, some famous residents were forced to leave 927 Fifth	13
Avenue in New York City. The red tail hawk Pale Male and his mate, Lola, had	29
moved into their digs on the ledge of the twelfth floor more than a decade earlier.	45
The couple had built an eight-foot-long nest on the ledge, and had hatched more	59
than two dozen offspring over the years. But some of the human residents of 927	74
complained about the hawks dropping leftovers of their meals in the street below.	87
Some complained about birdwatchers peering through binoculars at their building.	97
They had voted to have the nest removed, in the hope that the birds would move	113
across the street to the park.	119
The hawk couple's upcoming "eviction" won the attention of New Yorkers, some	131
of whom gathered in Central Park across the street to protest. For years, interested	145
observers had easily identified Pale Male by his unusually white feathers and	157
paused to watch him spin and dive to catch prey. Such evidence of nature in the	173
middle of a city was moving and inspiring.	181
As scheduled, workmen raised a scaffold and demolished the nest. For two weeks	194
after the eviction, Pale Male's fans continued to protest. The local Audubon Society	207
wrote the city's mayor, and protesters even confronted some of 927's famous	219
residents on the street.	223
The protesters' efforts were fruitful. By December 29, a twelve-foot metal	234
apparatus that was constructed to support a new nest had been installed where the	248
old hawk nest had been. It was hoped that Pale Male would be interested in the	264
new arrangement. In the next few weeks, he and Lola were spotted examining the	278
quarters, and everyone awaited a sign that they had decided to move back in.	292

© Pearson Education 6

Turn the page.

Answer the questions below.

1 The first event in the sequence of events in the selection appears to have happened sometime in

    A January 2005.

    B early December 2004.

    (C) the 1990s.

    D late December 2004.

2 What initiated the public's first awareness of the hawks?

    (F) People saw them and were interested in their behavior.

    G People used them as an excuse to spy on the residents of 927.

    H Word got out that their nest had been demolished.

    J Protesters began defending them.

3 What event directly led to the removal of the hawks' nest?

    A People began moving out of 927 Fifth Avenue.

    B The Audubon Society contacted the mayor.

    (C) Residents of 927 cast a vote.

    D The hawks' eating habits disturbed residents of 927.

4 What unanswered question in the selection is most important to the outcome?

    F Did anyone write a book about Pale Male and Lola?

    (G) Did Pale Male and Lola move into the metal nest?

    H Were the residents accepting of the birds' possible return?

    J Who funded the new metal nest and its placement?

5 What two options for a nest did the hawks have at the end of the selection?

They could live in the metal nest on the ledge of 927 or build a nest across the street in the park.

Read the selection. Then answer the questions that follow.

Ahead by Half

Saturday was unseasonably warm for Iowa in February. People were out	11
bicycling and walking their dogs. Neighbors' windows were open; Dale opened	22
his also and scrutinized his ravaged yard—dark islets of mud in a limitless ocean	37
of snow. Rather than undertake any outdoor activity, Dale committed himself to	49
some interior cleaning. He gathered an assortment of grocery bags and a couple of	63
durable boxes. He began by systematically sorting through drawers of clothes and	75
his many shelves and stacks of books. A faint layer of dust, almost like silt, lay	91
along the recesses of each bookshelf. He sneezed and dusted and vacuumed, and	104
sneezed some more. By midafternoon, Dale had filled two bags with clothing and	117
both boxes with books. "Two and two, pretty good," he reflected.	128
Dale loaded his truck and headed to the local thrift store. Under the carport for	143
drop-offs, he stopped and helped the attendant carry everything inside.	153
"Pretty nice out today," the attendant said, obviously wishing he were elsewhere.	165
"Yes," Dale said. "For some reason it made me want to clean."	177
Unfortunately, it also made Dale want to shop. He parked his car and wandered	191
idly inside.	193
He quickly noted the barely worn winter boots, and appealing all-wool sweaters.	205
Finally, cradling a light armload of two pairs of jeans, a fringed 1920s jacket he	220
would probably never have occasion to wear, and three cotton tee shirts bearing	233
superheroes, he found himself near the bookshelves. He chose several.	243
Once home, Dale used one grocery bag and one box to get his new things into	259
the house. . . . He came out ahead by half.	267

Turn the page.

Answer the questions below.

1 When did Dale decide it was a good day to clean?

   A the first thing after waking up on Saturday

   B before going to bed Friday night

   (C) after seeing how nice the weather was

   D upon returning home from a shopping trip

2 Which of the following occurs first in the selection?

   F The dust in the house makes Dale sneeze.

   (G) The neighbors' windows are open.

   H Dale looks at the muddy backyard.

   J Dale's own windows are opened.

3 Which of the following describes the order in which Dale appears to have shopped?

   A sweaters, blankets, jeans

   (B) boots, tee shirts, books

   C wall art, books, jeans

   D sweaters, vintage jackets, blankets

4 Explain how Dale came out ahead by half.

Dale took two grocery bags and two boxes into the thrift store and came home with one bag and one box full of items. So, in terms of cleaning the house and getting rid of things, Dale was "ahead" by "half" of the original amount.

5 Why might Dale's yard, based on the author's description of it, have inspired Dale to clean his house?

Answers may vary. Possible response: The yard is muddy and messy, and there is nothing Dale can do about it. Dale can, however, do something about the messiness inside of the house.

Read the selection. Then answer the questions that follow.

Getting the Message

Megan's older sister Tess was devastated by her cell phone bill. "I can't pay $100 | 15
to use my cell phone!" she lamented. | 22

Megan disliked cell phones. It was against the rules to bring one to school, and it | 38
pleased her when Eddie Wilson's phone ratted on him during homeroom by ringing | 51
loudly inside his backpack. | 55

Megan resented people walking along the street seemingly talking to themselves. | 66
"Can't they go anywhere alone?" Megan wondered. "When was the last time they | 79
heard a bird sing? Would they hear a car horn and know to get out of the way?" | 97

Now Tess was into "texting"—using her phone's dinky keyboard to send written | 110
messages to friends. "I know I'm charged ten cents a message," Tess wailed, "but it | 125
costs the same to read one as to send one, and it adds up fast!" | 140

"You recall that agreement you signed when you got your phone?" Megan asked. | 153
"Well, maybe reading the 'immediate messages' you get on it will teach you to read | 168
the small print when you sign contracts." | 175

Turn the page.

Answer the questions below.

1 Which generalization appears to be the theme of this story?

  A Talking things over is never a bad idea.

  B Don't spend more money than you have.

  C Never cross a street while talking on a cell phone.

  (D) Always read a contract through before signing it.

2 Which of these generalizations would Megan be most likely to make?

  F Everyone who has a cell phone has a large monthly bill.

  (G) Cell phones distract most people from the real world.

  H Text messages are the only smart use for cell phones.

  J Cell phones can block out all other noises.

3 Which of the following generalizations about cell phones would Tess be least likely to make?

  A Hearing from friends all day long lets you know you're liked.

  B Texting disturbs people around you less than talking does.

  (C) Cell phones allow you to let someone know you'll be late.

  D A large cell phone bill might persuade you to limit text messaging.

4 Explain why Tess's phone bill was bigger than she expected.

Tess didn't recognize how quickly the cost of sent and received messages would mount up.

Read the selection. Then answer the questions that follow.

A Learning Experience

Billy Jonstan sang rap songs while playing an electric guitar, and everyone	12
at school treated Billy like a celebrity. Sam, playing the big round lute that had	27
belonged to his father, had a different impact. Sam sang original ballads he wrote	41
about his favorite places in town. The lute's "voice" was soft and muted, and no one	57
seemed very eager to hear Sam perform. However, when Mr. Sargosta, his music	70
teacher, heard Sam, he encouraged him to record the ballads.	80
Because he was so young, one studio agreed to charge Sam just $50 an hour for	96
his recording session. Even with practically no "editing," it would take a minimum	109
of ten hours. Then producing each disc would cost $2.50, so if Sam ordered a	124
hundred, they would cost him $250.	130
Wiping out his $500 savings account required getting his parents' approval, and	142
Mr. Sargosta agreed to lend Sam $350. So Sam selected twelve of his best songs	157
and decided in what order to arrange them on the compact disc.	169
When the recording session was finished, he named the CD simply "Sam." He	182
persuaded his sister Kim to make a computer file of a photo she'd taken of him	198
to be used for the cover, and they printed out his lyrics and stapled little booklets	214
together to go inside the CD "jewel cases."	222
It was wonderfully exciting, but exhausting too. For a couple of months, he took	236
the CD around to record stores to ask them to sell it and approached disc jockeys to	253
ask them to play it. Sam was shy, and that part embarrassed him.	266
His classmates thought making his own CD was extremely cool. After three	278
months, Sam had sold enough copies at $10 each to pay Mr. Sargosta back and to	294
restore his bank account. He had learned a lot about producing a CD!	307

Turn the page.

Answer the questions below.

1 Except for Mr. Sargosta, how did people at school feel about Sam's music at first?

    A Most liked it better than Billy's rap.

    B Some thought it made Sam a celebrity.

    (C) No one paid much attention to it.

    D A few were ready to help produce it.

2 For Sam, making a CD was

    (F) very expensive.

    G somewhat expensive.

    H inexpensive.

    J pretty cheap.

3 Who was Sam's most consistent fan?

    A Sam's father

    B Billy Jonstan

    (C) Mr. Sargosta

    D Kim

4 From the story, it can be assumed that producing a successful CD is

    F a lot of luck and a little work.

    (G) a lot of luck and a lot of work.

    H likely if the music is good.

    J impossible without sound editing.

5 How did Sam feel about his music? What makes you think this?

Answers may vary. Possible response: Sam felt somewhat shy about his music, but he must have believed in it, otherwise he would not have been able to take Mr. Sargosta's suggestion or have put all of his savings into making the recording.

© Pearson Education 6

Read the selection. Then answer the questions that follow.

The Impossible Beast

Wildlife experts claim there have been no cougars east of the western states or	14
south of Canada for decades. They once inhabited much of the eastern United States	28
and are now "endangered" in North Carolina.	35
The thing is, I think I saw one this past winter. I was sprucing up an old house I'd	54
bought at the edge of a Midwestern town, and I wondered about all those huge paw	70
prints in the snow. They were too big for any canine, but they circled the place as if	88
a dog had been trying to get inside.	96
I'd resided here several months when I saw a magnificent animal sauntering	108
through my ragged meadow into the woods. It was approximately eight or nine	121
feet long from nose to tail, I estimated, with a back about four feet high. I never	138
saw its head, which was lowered in the deep grass. Its fur was a golden fawn color,	155
highlighted by the white sunlight—like photos I've seen of cougars. I still recall the	170
long, powerful tail that twitched behind the animal's muscular haunches.	180
In the hardware store I mentioned I'd seen a cougar heading into my woods, and	195
the news was greeted with compliments to my "vivid imagination." The only cougar	208
here, a professor who was buying a cordless drill said, was the rock star John	223
Cougar Mellencamp, who lived nearby, and he'd already dropped his middle name.	235
I've remained quiet about sightings since then to avoid embarrassment—that is, I	248
did see it again, prowling through the meadow as before. Once two guests of mine	263
were walking by the edge of the woods, and a huge wild animal with a long tail	280
sent them running breathless back to the house.	288
We all agreed that what we'd seen probably wasn't a cougar, but it sure looked	303
like one.	305

Turn the page.

- -

Answer the questions below.

1 Most people treated the speaker's claim that he had seen a cougar as a

  A simple mistake.

  (B) figment of the imagination.

  C bid for attention.

  D serious warning.

2 What does the speaker conclude that he saw in his meadow?

  (F) He does not know but assumes it was not a cougar.

  G He is positive that it was a cougar.

  H He admits that it was just something he imagined.

  J He implies that it was a vision caused by bright sunlight.

3 What details would support the generalization that most people sighting the animal would have thought it was a cougar?

  A North Carolina has declared cougars "endangered."

  B Paw prints too big to be a dog's circled the house.

  (C) The size and fur were like those of a cougar.

  D John Cougar Mellencamp lived nearby.

4 Explain why the speaker became embarrassed to say he'd seen a cougar.

The speaker became embarrassed because no one believed that he'd seen one earlier, and he knew that a cougar in the Midwest was unlikely.

5 In what two areas do most wildlife experts claim that cougars still live?

They live in the western United States and in Canada.

Read the selection. Then answer the questions that follow.

What's in a Name?

While playing soccer in the hall, Eddie saw the couple who was moving into	14
617. The man carried an open box, from which protruded an old hockey stick. The	29
woman followed, carrying a pair of ice skates, a basketball, and a jersey with the	44
name *Alex* across the back. When she dropped the ball, Eddie ran and picked it up.	60
"Here you go," Eddie said. "So Alex plays hockey? Me too."	71
"Alex will be here tomorrow," the woman volunteered.	79
"You know Alex?" the man asked, squinting inquiringly.	87
"Not yet, but he's into the same stuff I am," Eddie said.	99
The couple smiled knowingly at each other.	106
"So," Eddie said, "how old is Alex?"	113
"Alex is twelve and crazy about soccer and hockey," the woman said. "And	126
basketball." She offered Eddie her hand. "I'm Nonna Aminni, Alex's mother," she	138
said, "and this is Alex's dad, Jonathan."	145
Eddie happened to be in the hall with his soccer ball the next day, a Saturday,	161
when the Aminnis got off the elevator with a girl about his age. She had a long,	178
dark ponytail. She was wearing muddy and rumpled shorts and soccer cleats.	190
"Hi," Eddie gulped.	193
"Eddie," Mrs. Aminni said, "This is Alex."	200
Alex grinned and kicked the ball.	206

Answer the questions below.

1 What mistake does Eddie make that most people might have made?

  A He thinks Alex's parents are the movers.

  (B) He thinks that Alex is a boy.

  C He forgets to hold onto the soccer ball.

  D He thinks that Alex has a sister.

2 Eddie decides he is eager to meet Alex after he

  (F) sees hockey equipment in the box.

  G learns that he and Alex are the same age.

  H meets Alex's parents.

  J learns that Alex is a girl.

3 When do Alex's parents realize that Eddie thinks their daughter is a boy?

  A They never realize that Eddie thinks that.

  B They see how shocked he is when Alex gets off the elevator.

  (C) They know when Eddie says, "he's into the same stuff I am."

  D They know the minute Eddie asks about when Alex will get there.

4 How does Eddie know Alex's name before her parents say it?

He sees the name on the jersey Alex's mother is carrying.

Read the selection. Then answer the questions that follow.

Laying Claim to Lincoln

Three states claim Abraham Lincoln, our sixteenth President. He was born in	12
1809 in a log cabin in Kentucky, which claims it shaped Lincoln as "the common	27
man." The woman he loved, his best friend, and others of importance to him were	42
all native Kentuckians.	45
The Lincolns moved northward across the Ohio River in 1817, when Abe was	58
seven. He spent his boyhood on a humble Indiana farm that is now a national	73
monument. Abe's Indiana roots included very limited schooling, but he developed	84
an avid attraction to books, which he read by firelight.	94
Abe's mother, Nancy Hanks Lincoln, died when he was ten. Over time, his	107
stepmother, Sarah, became a devoted friend. Indiana claims it fostered Lincoln's	118
determination to learn and his ability to face tragedy.	127
After 1830, the family lived on a farm in Illinois. Abe split rails on the farm and	144
worked as a store clerk, a surveyor, and a postmaster. He studied and practiced law	159
in Springfield and entered politics, serving in the state and U.S. legislatures before	172
losing the race for senator to Stephen Douglas in 1858.	182
Robert Sherwood's 1938 Pulitzer Prize–winning play, *Abe Lincoln in Illinois,*	193
depicts Lincoln as a man struggling with his opposition to slavery and his	206
determination that it would not divide the Union. Lincoln's eloquent speeches	217
opposing slavery were winning national attention, but he said he would preserve the	230
Union even if that meant not freeing the slaves.	239
Lincoln, who was elected President in 1860, did free the slaves. The Civil War	253
began in 1861, and Lincoln led the North to victory, preserving the Union. Re-	267
elected in 1864, he was assassinated in Washington, D.C., shortly after the war	280
ended in 1865.	283
Edwin Stanton, his Secretary of War, said on that day, "Now he belongs to the	298
ages." He truly does—not just to the three states that are so proud to claim him.	315

© Pearson Education 6

Turn the page.

- -

Answer the questions below.

1 When did Abraham Lincoln most likely earn the nickname "the rail splitter"?

A when he lived in Kentucky

B while farming in Indiana

C after he moved to Illinois

D while serving as President

2 Where was Lincoln living when Sarah Lincoln became part of his life?

F in Kentucky

G in Indiana

H in Illinois

J in Washington, D.C.

3 When did Lincoln decide to go into politics?

A before he moved to Indiana

B when his mother died

C after he lost an election to Douglas

D after trying other occupations in Illinois

4 What generalization does this selection seem to support?

F Most politicians come from humble beginnings.

G A President can be from more than one state.

H In a Civil War, the side the President chooses has an advantage.

J Each state can claim at least one President.

5 What did Stanton mean by "Now he belongs to the ages"?

Lincoln had earned his place in history and would be remembered.

Read the selection. Then answer the questions that follow.

Stoke-on-Trent and Captain Smith

When the *Titanic* sailed for America in April of 1912, the English town	13
Stoke-on-Trent had just commissioned an artist to sculpt a statue of hometown hero	26
Edward John Smith. The intention was to honor the magnificent new ship's captain,	39
who had been at the helm of British passenger liners for more than thirty years.	54
By the time the statue was completed in 1914, Stoke didn't want it. Then, in	69
1985, when the wreckage of the *Titanic* was finally found at the bottom of the	84
Atlantic Ocean, the people of Stoke changed their minds again. But it was too late.	99
The "unsinkable" *Titanic* hit an iceberg on April 15, 1912, on its first voyage,	113
and went under in several hours. It hadn't been Captain Smith's fault that sections	127
of the double-hulled ship were actually only one layer thick, but eventually many	140
blamed him for its sinking. The *Titanic* was cruising full speed through a sea he	155
knew was full of ice. The captain happened not to be at the helm when the gigantic	172
ship collided with an iceberg, and he was surprisingly cautious responding to the	185
emergency.	186
Captain Smith knew there weren't enough lifeboats for all the passengers. The	198
crew realized the ship was sinking, but the captain was reluctant to inform the	212
passengers with specifics. He commanded, "Stay calm. Be British."	221
The traditional and valiant captain went down with his ship, and his reputation	234
sank too. The people of Stoke rejected the finished statue, and the town of	248
Lichfield, twenty-five miles away, obtained it and placed it in a park. It honors	262
Smith's "great heart, brave life, and heroic death," and is designated as a national	276
monument.	277
After the sunken *Titanic* was found, a number of tourists visited Stoke hoping to	291
see Captain Smith "in the bronze." Stoke wasn't able to get the statue back. Instead	306
tourists had to be directed to Lichfield.	313

© Pearson Education 6

Turn the page.

Answer the questions below.

1   **What made the town of Stoke-on-Trent decide it didn't want the statue of Captain Smith?**

    A   Captain Smith was given command of the *Titanic*.

    (B) The *Titanic* sank on its first voyage.

    C   It was discovered that the *Titanic* didn't have enough lifeboats.

    D   The statue was designated a national monument.

2   **The selection suggests that the *Titanic's* sinking was due to the**

    F   job of captain being given to an inexperienced sailor.

    G   hometown folks turning their backs on Smith.

    H   *Titanic* traveling through seas filled with ice.

    (J) ship having been made with a single-layered hull.

3   **What does the selection suggest led to the town of Stoke-on-Trent wanting the statue after all?**

    A   Captain Smith heroically remained with his ship as it sank.

    B   The statue was finally completed and ready to be displayed.

    C   The town of Lichfield wanted it, which made it seem desirable.

    (D) The recovered remains of the *Titanic* led to new interest in Smith.

4   **What two changes were probably made in ocean liners built after the *Titanic*?**

Ocean liners built after the Titanic probably had double-layered hulls. They may have had more lifeboats and fewer passengers.

5   **What, according to the selection, did Edward John Smith do that most good captains would probably have done?**

Captain Smith stayed with his ship as it sank.

Name _____

Read the selection. Then answer the questions that follow.

Letting Them Down Gently

Albert Kolk was flying his grandson and two of the boy's friends up to Canada.	15
Suddenly the plane began to plunge earthward. Mr. Kolk pulled on a red lever, and	30
a rocket blasted something out of the plane and through a back window!	43
A parachute as big as a house opened above them. It was tied to the plane's nose,	60
wings, and tail, and the plane floated safely to the ground.	71
Back in 2004, the idea of a parachute for a plane was new. Yet more than five	88
hundred small planes had one. Not all of those needed in emergencies had worked,	102
but there were happy endings. One pilot reported that his damaged plane landed so	116
gently in a field under a parachute, some glass ornaments he had on board were not	132
broken.	133
People wondered whether larger planes would ever have parachutes. Could	143
parachutes be made huge and strong enough to hold up an airliner's eighty thousand	157
pounds? Would they work at six hundred miles per hour? Would astronauts ever	170
ride in shuttles that had their own parachutes?	178

Turn the page.

Answer the questions below.

1 How does a plane's parachute get out of the plane and open?

(A) A rocket blasts it out of the back of the plane.

B It floats out of the plane when it is needed.

C It explodes out of the plane's nose.

D The plane's spiral spins it out into the air.

2 This selection seems to suggest that this technique could work on most passenger jets if the

F passengers each had a parachute.

(G) parachutes could be big enough.

H emergencies were not too severe.

J planes were to fly much slower.

3 What does the selection suggest a plane ride under one of these parachutes would be like?

A The plane would spiral to the ground.

B It would be like riding a rocket.

(C) It would be a rather gentle, floating ride.

D It would feel like a dog chasing its tail.

4 At present, does it seem likely that passenger airplanes will soon have parachutes? Use information in the passage to explain your answer.

No, it does not seem likely. The parachutes on small planes do not work all the time, and there are still more questions than answers about using parachutes for other types of aircraft.

Read the selection. Then answer the questions that follow.

An Opening to Paradise

Just listing the unusual plant and animal life here is like a trip through paradise.	15
These plants and animals are all found in northwest Ohio in the "Oak Openings."	29
The 130-square-mile region is "One of America's Last Great Places." It's not a	42
wilderness. Parts of it were once cleared for farming, but its sandy, acidic soil kept	57
most settlers from farming there. So most of it remained undeveloped.	68
Ten thousand years ago, the area was at the southern edge of a great glacial lake.	84
The glacier melted, and the lake drew back, leaving five to fifteen feet of sand to	100
mix with the clay soil. Time left a narrow finger of land, made of dry and acidic	117
soil, on which more than one thousand species of plant life and abundant animal	131
kingdoms flourish.	133
There are a few farms and homes in the area. However, four thousand acres are	148
now conserved as public parks and other public areas. Some people who live in the	163
Openings are cooperating with the government to maintain the ecosystem there.	174
Understandably, such a unique place is an appealing place to live. Developers hope	187
to pack new houses and stores right up against the Openings, and commercial	200
growth will have an impact on and could eliminate the Oak Openings.	212
An effort to protect this precious area while making it accessible so the public	226
can enjoy its incredible variety of plant and animal life never ends. It requires	240
an ongoing awareness campaign. "Stewardship" of Ohio's Oak Openings means	250
educating everyone about its irreplaceable value.	256
Visitors quickly understand how preserved it is when they see the bogs and living	270
sand dunes. When they walk under its pin oak and black oak trees or spot the rare	287
lark sparrow and the spotted turtle or blue-spotted salamander, they realize. Scarlet	299
tanagers and Karner blue butterflies flit over fields of blue and yellow wildflowers	312
and inspire people to commit to maintaining one of the last great places.	325

© Pearson Education 6

Turn the page.

Answer the questions below.

1 Developers would probably argue against the conclusion that

    A everyone would like to live in a modern development.

    B people are more important than butterflies or salamanders.

    (C) all wild, undeveloped areas should be kept that way.

    D humans are a part of the animal kingdom too.

2 This selection suggests that a geographic region with greatly varied plant life is likely to have

    F many types of birds.

    G few people living near it.

    H careful development and farming.

    (J) dry and acidic soil.

3 The article notes that the problem of maintaining the Oak Openings is due to the fact that

    (A) people always want to live near beautiful areas.

    B too much sand can spoil the soil.

    C no one wants to accept stewardship for the region.

    D people are too aware of its great public value.

4 Why did early settlers probably not settle in Oak Openings?

    F The bogs were very dangerous.

    (G) The sandy soil was bad for farming.

    H It has remained under water until recently.

    J Wildlife frightened most people away.

5 Why might birdwatchers in particular enjoy Oak Openings?

One or more of the birds that live there are rare.

© Pearson Education 6

Read the selection. Then answer the questions that follow.

A Wide Range of Poets

You might think that the last place to hear poetry would be around a campfire	15
with cowboys. It turns out that cowboys are as poetic as any folks you can gather.	31
They sustain poetry as it was invented and intended—as the earliest form of story-	46
telling and entertainment. Cowboys began reciting poems before there was radio or	58
television. Many cowboy poems, like ancient ballads, folktales, and American tall	69
tales, were not written down.	74
Cowboys are often shown in Western movies as tough, no-nonsense guys who	86
hide their feelings. Expressing themselves openly in poetry is one of the last things	100
you would expect from them, but they often like to share their poems.	113
In 1985 a U.S. agency helped organize the first convention to honor cowboy	126
poetry. About one hundred cowboy and cowgirl poets from fifteen states gathered	138
and read their original poems aloud. They also read old favorites they had learned	152
from books and by listening. Cowpokes have responded enthusiastically ever since.	163
At the Annual National Cowboy Poets Gathering, there are big shows and dozens	176
of meetings in different halls. Meanwhile, hundreds of cowboy poetry books have	188
been published, and numerous Web sites are maintained. There is an international	200
society and a dozen or more smaller gatherings each year.	210
What do cowboy poets write about? Well, they tend to be a sentimental bunch,	224
and many, but not all, of their poems are about their work and their animals. Some	240
even sing the praises of cows.	246
It is not unusual to hear a cowboy or cowgirl poet recite something like this:	261

Riding the range after a day	267
With the horses and dogs that I love,	275
I'm thankin' my lucky stars that I may	283
Sit under that soft light above	289
And know that the hard day tomorrow will bring—	298
With its dry, dusty, cold drivin' air—	305
The challenge to face just any old thing	313
And breathe deep from the freedom we share.	321

Turn the page.

- -

Answer the questions below.

1 One reason given that cowboys became poets was that

   Ⓐ they had no radio or television for entertainment.

   B someone started an annual convention for them.

   C poets were needed to appear in Western movies.

   D their stories were not being written down.

2 This selection assumes that most people would not consider cowboys to be

   F sentimental about wide open spaces.

   G interested in gatherings of any kind.

   Ⓗ interested in writing poetry.

   J proud about the kind of work they do.

3 The selection suggests that often cowboy poetry tends to focus on

   A ancient stories.

   B radio and television shows.

   C what is learned from books.

   Ⓓ their work and animals.

4 The poem quoted mentions horses and dogs. What other elements in the poem are probably common in cowboy poetry?

Answers may vary. Possible response: Other common elements are probably working outdoors, facing the weather, and the sense of freedom and space.

5 How is much of cowboy poetry similar to the old ballads and tales?

Cowboy poetry, like old ballads and tales, is often shared orally and sometimes is not written down.

Read the selection. Then answer the questions that follow.

A Long Day!

Time is confusing in Spain these days. Working people there follow two very	13
different time schedules. Traditionally, a Spanish workday starts at 9 A.M. and is not	27
over until 8 P.M., with a long break beginning about 2 P.M. and lasting two to three	44
hours.	45
During that break, stores and offices close. People used to go home for naps or	60
siestas, but now most workers take very long, relaxed lunch hours instead. Then	73
it's back to work until 8 P.M., when they go home and sit down to dinner at about	91
10 P.M.	93
However, many Spaniards are trying to establish work schedules more familiar	104
in the United States—from about 8 A.M. until 5 P.M. These parents would like to	120
get home in time to relax with their children, who are home from school. Often,	135
children and their parents are both fed and ready for bed by 8 or 9 P.M.—that is,	153
before people keeping the traditional schedule are home. Confusing? Yes, and it	165
may not be straightened out soon. Tradition tends to prevail in Spain, and many	179
Spaniards aren't ready to think of 8 P.M. as "bedtime."	189

Turn the page.

Answer the questions below.

1 The writer of this selection assumes that the reader will find the traditional Spanish workday

    A appealing.

    B tiring.

    C familiar.

    (D) unusual.

2 Children who have parents following the traditional workday schedule in Spain probably

    F go to schools that run very late as well.

    G don't see much of their parents on workdays.

    (H) eat dinner later.

    J attend schools near the places their parents work.

3 How does the time a traditional Spanish workday starts compare to the time most other people start their days?

    (A) The two kinds of schedules start at around the same time.

    B The traditional workday starts a lot earlier than the other schedule.

    C The traditional workday starts a lot later than the other schedule.

    D The traditional workday starts with a siesta.

4 Explain why workers on the traditional schedule think of 8 P.M. as "afternoon."

They are just finishing their workday, and have yet to go
home to enjoy what they consider the evening.

Read the selection. Then answer the questions that follow.

A Very Practical Idea

Most towns have something they are known for, and Farmington, known as	12
the home of the University of Maine, is also "the earmuff capital of the world."	27
Years ago, nearly a fourth of all the world's earmuffs were made there. They aren't	42
manufactured in Farmington anymore, but it is the place where earmuffs were	54
invented in 1873, and every year the townspeople there have a parade in December	68
on "Chester Greenwood Day."	72
Chester was fifteen when he invented earmuffs, and he wasn't one of those	85
people who said, "Good idea. I should do something about it." It took Chester two	100
years to get his invention patented, and after that he set up a factory in Farmington	116
to make earmuffs. Being something of an inventor all his life, he invented machines	130
to ensure that the manufacture of Greenwood's Champion Ear Protectors would be	142
consistent and mostly automatic.	146
The idea for earmuffs came to Chester while he was ice skating. He'd tried to	161
protect his sensitive ears by wrapping an itchy scarf around his head. That proved	175
too awkward, so, back home, Chester cut out ear-sized pieces of the scarf and got	190
his grandmother to sew them together to fit over wire loops at the ends of a curved	207
wire that perched on his head.	213
Chester himself went on to invent other things, such as the mechanical mouse	226
trap, shock absorbers for automobiles, the whistling teakettle, and other useful	237
things. Interest in earmuffs eventually waned, though fashion designers have revived	248
it by creating very stylish earmuffs to go with skiing outfits and other winter wear.	263
But fashion earmuffs are not made in Farmington.	271
In the parade on Chester Greenwood Day, you will see earmuffs on everything	284
that moves, including people, animals, and cars. In Maine in winter, it's usually	297
cold enough to demonstrate what a good idea that Farmington teenager had!	309

© Pearson Education 6

Turn the page.

- -

Answer the questions below.

1 How do the people of Farmington appear to feel about being "the earmuff capital of the world"?

   A They wish people would forget about Chester Greenwood Day.

   B They regret that there is no earmuff factory there anymore.

   (C) They think it is fun and have a good time with the annual celebration.

   D They wish the world would give Farmington the credit it deserves.

2 What kind of a person does Chester Greenwood seem to have been?

   F He was not nearly as clever as he thought he was.

   (G) He was a bright, creative, and determined boy.

   H He was more interested in selling than in creating things.

   J Once he invented something, he forgot about it.

3 Before Chester Greenwood invented earmuffs, what had to happen?

   A He had to demonstrate that he was a good inventor.

   B A factory to produce what he invented had to be found.

   C His state had to recognize how talented he was.

   (D) He had to be out in the cold with his sensitive ears.

4 Why do the people of Farmington and Maine hold an annual parade in honor of earmuffs?

   (F) Chester Greenwood helped make their town and state special.

   G They are hoping someone will get the earmuff factory going again.

   H They feel they must prove where earmuffs were invented.

   J Other inventors need that encouragement to do their best work.

5 When an invention is created, what is the intent of the inventor, and who benefits from a successful invention?

An inventor is usually trying to solve his or her own problem when he or she invents something, and a successful invention benefits the inventor and many other people, making their lives easier and more comfortable.

Read the selection. Then answer the questions that follow.

Fearing Extinction

In April of 1999, after hunting turkeys in the Pearl River Wildlife Management	13
Area in southeastern Louisiana, college student David Kulivan came out of the	25
forest and reported watching something unusual at close range for a quarter of an	39
hour. His report excited naturalists across the nation!	47
Soon planes were scouting the huge forest area to begin plans for a scientific,	61
intensive search. It took over a year to enlist the best experts for the expedition.	76
They would venture into deep bayous and flooded forest bottoms, carrying cameras,	88
recorders, and computers.	91
Meanwhile, people were discussing David and his report. He did not seem to be	105
staging a hoax, but was he just hopeful and merely believing what he wanted to see?	121
This excursion was not the first dedicated attempt to observe the ivory-billed	133
woodpecker, and no one had yet been successful. It had been more than fifty years	148
since a credible sighting of this, the largest of the woodpeckers, even though claims	162
of sightings had been made approximately every decade, giving people hope that	174
the ivory-billed was not, as most feared, extinct.	182
Reported sightings of the ivory-billed are usually assumed to be sightings of the	195
pileated woodpecker, a beautiful large woodpecker that is similar to, but smaller	207
than, the ivory-billed. Many pileated woodpeckers inhabit areas of the United States	219
They are, like the ivory-billed, a combination of black and white.	230
Both the male and female pileated woodpeckers have dramatic red crests, while	242
only the ivory-billed male has one. There are other distinctions. The ivory-billed	254
has a longer whitish bill, which explains its name. There are also differences in the	269
"chin" and other markings, which David Kulivan knew and noted when describing	281
what he saw.	284
The excursion in 2002 did not confirm that the ivory-billed is not extinct. Still,	298
most people believe—want to believe—that David's report was a credible sighting	311
of this mysterious, elusive bird.	316

© Pearson Education 6

Turn the page.

- -

Answer the questions below.

1 The details in the second paragraph suggest that when experts do scientific studies they

   A need to ask for permission.

   B need to spend a year in college.

   C need to make claims of sightings before venturing on location.

   (D) need to go to the location equipped with necessary tools.

2 The selection makes it clear that

   F there have been many credible sightings of the ivory-billed woodpecker in the last fifty years.

   (G) the excursion could not confirm the sighting.

   H Kulivan's sighting of the ivory-billed woodpecker was a hoax.

   J the ivory-billed woodpecker is extinct.

3 The details in paragraphs 5 and 6 lead us to conclude that the ivory-billed woodpecker and the pileated woodpecker

   (A) are different in many ways.

   B live in areas outside the United States.

   C are the same size and colors.

   D have long, whitish bills.

4 Why did Kulivan's report raise more interest than other reports in the last fifty years?

Kulivan's sighting seemed credible because he watched the woodpecker for a quarter of an hour and noted a lot of details about its appearance, all of which matched the characteristics of the ivory-billed woodpecker.

5 Based on the selection and its title, what can we conclude about all the reported sightings of the ivory-billed woodpecker?

People who make such reports are usually mistaken, but enthusiasts and naturalists still hope to prove that the ivory-billed woodpecker is not extinct.

Read the selection. Then answer the questions that follow.

Disposable Phones

Toy maker Randi Altschul was driving her car one day while talking on her	14
cell phone. Suddenly the voice on the other end began to crackle and fade. She	29
wanted to toss her cell phone out the window. She hesitated because a cell phone is	45
expensive to replace. That was when the idea occurred to her to make a cell phone	61
that was disposable.	64
Technologists built Altschul's very thin cell phone out of a special plastic.	76
The phone is about three times as thick as a bank card and is a trifold. Along the	94
inside of the plastic is a long, twisting circuit. The first version of the disposable	109
phone will have sixty minutes of time on it. When the time is up, the phone can be	127
recharged or recycled.	130
Altschul believes people will buy this new disposable phone. It is convenient,	142
portable, and can easily be replaced.	148

© Pearson Education 6

Answer the questions below.

1 What is the main idea of this selection?

   A Plastic is the most popular material for phones.

   B Developing ideas into products is simple.

   C Ideas for new products can come from anyone.

   (D) The solution to a problem can be a new product.

2 Randi Altschul believed that people would buy her phones because they are

   F inexpensive compared to other phones.

   (G) convenient to use and could be recycled.

   H as small as bank cards.

   J equipped with a superior circuit system.

3 Randi Altschul assumed that Americans would like her phone's design because

   A other cell phones are too big and awkward.

   (B) all cell phone users sometimes feel similarly frustrated.

   C if the circuit is broken, the phone can be tossed.

   D they can get a new phone after only one hour.

4 Randi Altschul is a toy maker. How do you think this influenced her decision to make the disposable phone?

Answers may vary. Possible response: Randi Altschul was probably used to working with things that were fun, easy to use, and not meant to last a lifetime.

© Pearson Education 6

Read the selection. Then answer the questions that follow.

Where Ideas Come From

Have you ever wondered where ideas for inventions come from? Inventors think	12
about building new things and gadgets all the time. However, inventors don't always	25
come up with their ideas alone. Sometimes ideas for an invention bloom from a	39
conversation with a friend, coworker, or stranger. This happened to Thomas Adams	51
in 1869.	53
Adams had been a photographer, but he was trying to become an inventor. At	67
the time, the Mexican Commander, General Santa Anna, was a guest in his house	81
on Staten Island. Santa Anna knew that Adams wanted to be an inventor so he	96
offered a suggestion. He suggested Adams use a rubbery Mexican substance called	108
chicle to make rubber tires. Adams liked Santa Anna's suggestion, and he began to	122
experiment. Alas, all his tire experiments failed. Then he tried to make rubber toys	136
and rain boots using chicle. Those attempts failed too. For a year, none of Thomas'	151
ideas worked. He was frustrated. He wanted to use the chicle in a new item, but he	168
didn't have any fresh ideas.	173
Adams finally recalled that Santa Anna often chewed chicle for pleasure and to	186
exercise his jaw muscles. Adams had never tried that. He rushed to his laboratory,	200
popped a piece of chicle into his mouth, and began to chew.	212
Elsewhere in the United States, chewing gum was also in the making. The	225
Fleer brothers had used an extract from the Sapodilla tree, covering it with a hard	240
white coating. They did not market the gum widely, though. The Curtis brothers	253
in Maine experimented with spruce tree resin, switching to paraffin later. Adams	265
experimented with putting licorice in the chicle gum and manufactured the first	277
flavored chewing gum in the United States. It was called "Black Jack" and came	291
in the shape of a stick rather than a ball or chunk. People loved it, and Adams was	309
officially an inventor.	312

© Pearson Education 6

Turn the page.

Answer the questions below.

1 The main idea of this selection is

   A chewing gum has been around for many years.

   B an inventor has to be smart.

   (C) great ideas of inventors can be inspired by others.

   D all chewing gum is made from *chicle*.

2 Santa Anna most likely gave Adams the suggestion to use *chicle* to make tires because as an inventor Adams seemed

   F unable to create ideas.

   G distracted.

   H on the wrong track.

   (J) open to input from others.

3 Why was Adams's gum probably more successful than that of the Fleer or Curtis brothers?

   (A) Flavoring the gum made it more pleasing to chew.

   B The Curtis brothers used paraffin.

   C The Fleer brothers were bad at marketing.

   D Gum that came in chunks was less marketable.

4 Based on what the selection tells you about Adams, what do you think inventors must not do in order to succeed?

   F remain open to suggestions

   G learn from their failures

   (H) give up on a project idea

   J work hard every day

5 What was General Santa Anna's role in Adams's success, and would you describe it as major or minor?

Answers may vary. Possible response: General Santa Anna played a minor role in Adams's success in that he happened to suggest *chicle* as a substance worth experimenting with. He did not do any of the work, however, that led to the invention of flavored chewing gum.

Read the selection. Then answer the questions that follow.

In the Hive

Early beehives were simply shelters shaped like boxes or "hives." As beekeepers	12
learned about bee colonies' needs and the interior layout of a hive, hive structures	26
were modernized to make gathering honey safer for the interior architecture of the	39
hive. For example, there is one queen, and she stays in a "brood nest" where she	55
lays all of her eggs. The nest is in a safe location. This was at the center of the early	75
hives, and the drone (worker) bees built "honeycombs" along the sides. In later	88
hives, bars were stretched over the open top. The bars and the attached, dangling	102
combs could be lifted out without disturbing the brood nest below. Modern hives	115
are boxes that have removable trays. The tray structure allows the beekeeper to	128
check on the health of the bees and gather honey without disturbing the business of	143
the hive. It also allows the beekeeper to start a new hive without greatly disrupting	158
the previous one.	161
One basic goal of the beekeeper is to keep the bees calm. The beekeeper aims to	177
provide a safe and productive environment for the bees to live in and make honey.	192
When working with a colony, beekeepers do not wear dark, rough, or woolly	205
fabric or perfume or lotion. Those fabrics and unusual odors alarm the bees and	219
can induce "swarming behavior." Swarming behavior occurs when the odor of bee	231
venom excites other bees to sting; a mass of bees excite themselves into a frenzy.	246
Beekeepers do occasionally experience stings when handling the colony. One way	257
they can protect themselves is by wearing a veil over the face and head or even	273
a full beekeeping suit, a puffy white outfit that makes the beekeeper look like an	288
astronaut.	289

© Pearson Education 6

Turn the page.

Answer the questions below.

1 "In the Hive" is mainly about
  (A) hives and beekeepers.
  B the behavior of drone bees.
  C ways beekeepers avoid being stung.
  D the production of honey.

2 The structure of hives was changed to
  F keep bees from swarming.
  G protect the bees from weather.
  H keep the bees enclosed in the hive.
  (J) allow for the safe gathering of honey.

3 The biggest problem with early hives was that
  A the brood nest was too close to the sides.
  B beekeepers got stung reaching in.
  (C) the hive's architecture was easily damaged.
  D the hives could not be easily moved.

4 Why do you think bees become agitated when they smell bee venom?

They know that a threat must be near if one or more members of the hive used their stingers and emitted venom.

_____

_____

_____

5 Do you think a good beekeeper would be more likely to check a hive daily or weekly? Explain your answer.

A good beekeeper would be more likely to check a hive weekly because the goal is not to disturb the bees any more than is necessary.

_____

_____

Read the selection. Then answer the questions that follow.

Can Cats Think?

Most people agree that cats are intelligent animals. Some cats appear to be more	14
intelligent than others. But many people insist that all cats behave as if they are	29
thinking things through.	32
Certain cat behaviors suggest that cats are thinking. By nature, cats are cautious	45
and able to sense when a threat is nearby. They are also very curious. They love	61
to explore new environments and locations. They will nap in half-open drawers, in	74
empty grocery sacks, or on a sweater on a chair. Finally, cats can solve problems.	89
If a cat is cold, he will sit under a lamp. If he wants to catch a squirrel, he will wait	110
under a tree. Most cats that live with people are smart enough to get the people to	127
open the door for them. They go outside to roam and come back in whenever they	143
want.	144

Turn the page.

Answer the questions below.

1 Why do you think the author wrote "Can Cats Think?"

   A to tell funny facts about cats

   (B) to discuss how cats show intelligence

   C to convince the reader to like cats

   D to show how living with people changes cats

2 The author writes, "Some cats appear to be more intelligent than others." Which words tell the reader that this is an opinion?

   F some cats

   (G) appear to be

   H more intelligent

   J than others

3 The tone of the author of the selection can best be described as

   A serious.

   B funny.

   C scientific.

   (D) friendly.

4 Why do you think the author used a question for the title?

Answers may vary. Possible response: The question gets the reader thinking about the subject even before the reading begins.

Read the selection. Then answer the questions that follow.

Kenaf: The Wonder Plant

Kenaf (ka NEF) is indeed a wonder plant. It is an ancient crop grown in Africa | 15

for four thousand years. The Egyptians used it as food for their animals. A | 29

member of the cotton family, kenaf will grow anywhere cotton grows, and it grows | 43

extremely rapidly. In about five months when it is ready for harvest, the plant is | 58

twelve to fourteen feet tall. In the southern United States, where the winter is not | 73

too cold, kenaf farmers often have two growing seasons at the same time farmers of | 88

other crops have one. Both the inside and the outside of the tall cane-like stalk can | 104

be made into different products. | 109

Kenaf has been in the United States since the mid-1950s. Several government | 121

agencies and universities have studied kenaf for many years. Research reveals that | 133

this single plant has a variety of uses. The many products that can be made from | 149

kenaf include cooking oil, bedding for horses, food for cattle, cat litter, fabric, and | 163

paper. | 164

This hardy plant is truly remarkable. It can be made into many different items | 178

whose quality is superior to other materials. For example, kenaf paper is stronger | 191

than paper made from southern pine trees. It also costs less to make, and the | 206

process is easier on the environment. One government study states that for the same | 220

number of acres planted in kenaf and in pine trees, kenaf produces about four times | 235

more fiber than pine trees. Also, it takes from seven to forty years for pines to grow | 252

tall enough to be harvested. Kenaf can be harvested in only five months. | 265

Turn the page.

Answer the questions below.

1 Based on the information in the selection, which is most likely true of the author?

   A The author grows kenaf for profit.

   (B) The author thinks kenaf is a valuable crop.

   C The author thinks kenaf is the grain of the future.

   D The author wants readers to buy kenaf products.

2 Which of these best supports the title of the selection?

   F Kenaf will grow anywhere cotton grows.

   G Kenaf has been in the United States since the mid-1950s.

   (H) Research reveals that this single plant has a variety of uses.

   J It takes seven to forty years for pines to grow tall enough to be harvested.

3 What does the author use to convince readers about kenaf's value?

   A humorous sayings

   (B) factual information

   C personal stories

   D historical records

4 The author wrote, "This hardy plant is truly remarkable." Which of the following states the same opinion?

   F Kenaf can be harvested in only five months.

   G Several government agencies have studied kenaf.

   H Kenaf is a member of the cotton family.

   (J) Kenaf is indeed a wonder plant.

5 Did the author convince you that kenaf paper is better than pine paper? Explain.

Answers may vary. Students should support their answers with good reasons.

Name _____

Read the selection. Then answer the questions that follow.

Bats: An Asset

Many people think of bats as blind, daring creatures that swoop out of nowhere at | 15
night, making an odd screeching noise and aiming at a person's hair or neck. None | 30
of this is true. The bat's reputation as a scary Halloween creature is undeserved. | 44
Bats are useful, peaceful animals that would probably prefer not to encounter | 56
people at all. | 59

Bats fly at night, locating things by a "sonar" system. That is, they sense | 73
the sound waves from living and non-living things. They're out primarily to | 85
hunt insects, the main part of their diet. In fact, bats improve the environmental | 99
conditions for people by devouring insects such as mosquitoes. A colony of | 111
only 150 large brown bats can gobble almost thirty-three million rootworms in | 123
a summer, giving crops the protection necessary for a good harvest. A Mexican | 136
colony of twenty million free-tailed bats typically eats two hundred tons of insects | 149
every night. Bats are also a source of pollination and spreading of seeds for plants | 164
such as bananas, dates, and figs. Clearly, bats are an asset rather than a threat. | 179

Bat conservationists, concerned about different bat species becoming extinct, | 188
popularized "bat houses" in the United States in the 1980s. Over time, they | 201
discovered that bats prefer to roost a quarter mile or less from a stream, river, or | 217
large lake and to be near orchards, fields used to grow crops, or the woods. The | 233
best-liked houses were stained dark and placed in a location that got at least four | 248
hours of sun per day. One study showed that the higher up a bat house is placed, | 265
the more likely it is to be occupied. Bats clearly prefer to keep their distance from | 281
people and to socialize amongst themselves. | 287

© Pearson Education 6

Turn the page.

Answer the questions below.

1 Which of the following best describes the author's argument about bats?

   A Bats must be kept in bat houses away from people.

   B Bats are tame enough that people could pet them.

   (C) Bats are harmless and helpful to people.

   D Houses should be provided for all bats in the United States.

2 Why did the author most likely discuss what some species of bats eat?

   F to show that bats do not eat meat

   G to avoid saying what other species of bats eat

   H to explain why bats fly only at night

   (J) to imply what a large number of insects the bats eat

3 Based on the selection, which of the following is a statement of opinion?

   A Bats fly at night, guided by sound waves.

   (B) Bats are an asset, not a threat.

   C The most successful bat houses are set high.

   D Bats prefer to live near fresh water.

4 Does the author appear to think that bat houses are a good idea? Why or why not?

Answers may vary. Possible response: The author appears to think that bat houses are a good idea. The author describes what makes a bat house attractive to bats, implying that it is worth building more houses like these.

5 Based on the information in the selection, what characteristics of a bat house do you think the author would suggest as not appealing to bats?

Answers may vary. Possible responses: The author would probably say that bats would not be attracted to houses that were light in color, far from any body of fresh water, away from orchards, fields, or the woods, or that were too low to the ground.

© Pearson Education 6

102

Read the selection. Then answer the questions that follow.

Mighty Joe Bob and Jack

Mighty Joe Bob is a distinguished character, bigger than life, who roamed the	13
Texas Hill Country in years gone by. Nobody ever actually saw Mighty Joe Bob,	27
but every rancher around knows who he was and what he and his dog, Jack, did.	43
They know that Mighty Joe Bob was responsible for bringing river water to the Hill	58
Country.	59
A long time ago there was no natural water in the hills. The whole area was	75
parched under the blistering sun until Mighty Joe Bob gave Jack a bone. Jack	89
gnawed his bone for three days but ate only a third of it. When Jack dug a hole to	108
bury the rest, he struck a pool of underground water. Freezing cold water bubbled	122
from the ground and flowed freely.	128
So today, there is cold, clean water snaking through the Hill Country.	140

Turn the page.

© Pearson Education 6

Answer the questions below.

1 The author's statement that nobody ever saw Mighty Joe Bob most likely suggests that

(A) Mighty Joe Bob might be a myth.

B Mighty Joe Bob was good at hiding from people.

C Some people lied about having seen him.

D Jack's owner was someone else.

2 Because Jack dug a hole for his bone,

F ranchers know where to find bones.

G he was able to save two-thirds of it for a later time.

(H) water sprang from the ground.

J the bone polluted the water.

3 Because every rancher seemed to know the story of Mighty Joe Bob and Jack, you can assume that

(A) ranchers all passed the story around.

B ranchers all used the water.

C ranchers built dams to contain the water.

D ranchers appreciate what Mighty Joe Bob and Jack did.

4 Why do you think there was no natural water in the Hill Country until Jack dug the hole?

Answers may vary. Possible response: No one had thought to dig below the surface for an underground spring.

Name _____

Read the selection. Then answer the questions that follow.

Franco's Choice

Franco awoke as usual, got dressed, and headed for school like he always did.	14
While riding his bicycle, he thought about how routine everything was.	25
Three blocks from school, Franco stopped at the corner realizing he had a choice.	39
He could go straight as always, or he could turn left and take the longer path to	56
school. He needed some variety, so Franco turned left.	65
Franco noticed a white automobile speeding toward the school, and he thought	77
the driver ought to slow down. Unexpectedly, he saw something that made him skid	91
to a stop. He saw an object soar from the car window and land in the tall weeds	109
near the sidewalk. He sped to the site where the object had landed. There, Franco	124
scoured the weeds until he found a man's billfold, and thought it might have been	139
stolen. Thanks to police shows on TV, he knew he shouldn't touch anything that	153
was stolen, so he used his lunch bag to pick up the billfold. Franco then rushed to	170
school. He marched into the office and turned in the billfold.	181
Later, Mr. Jones, the principal, found Franco in the lunchroom eating his	193
sandwich. "May I have your attention?" he shouted above the lunchroom noise.	205
Everyone grew quiet. "I want to tell you about Franco," Mr. Jones said. Franco	219
choked on his tuna sandwich. "Franco found a billfold and brought it to the office.	234
We called the police and learned the billfold had been stolen. Thank you, Franco,	248
for being a model citizen. And here is a fifty dollar reward from the billfold's	263
owner. Let's all give Franco a big hand." The lunchroom rocked with thunderous	276
applause. Mr. Jones was proud of Franco, and Franco felt proud too.	288

© Pearson Education 6

Turn the page.

Answer the questions below.

1 Based on the reaction of Mr. Jones and others in the lunchroom, Franco will probably be known as a

   A bicyclist.

   B fool.

   Ⓒ hero.

   D tattletale.

2 Franco probably rushed to find the billfold in the weeds because he was

   Ⓕ curious.

   G worried.

   H confident.

   J scared.

3 Why do you think the author wrote this story?

   A to persuade the reader to change daily routines

   B to inform the reader of ways to get a reward

   C to express concern over crime

   Ⓓ to inform the reader of the importance of our choices

4 Because Franco took a different way to school, he

   F decided always to use that route.

   Ⓖ had an unexpected experience.

   H was late to school.

   J got to meet Mr. Jones.

5 The title of the story is "Franco's Choice." What do you think Franco learned from his choice?

Answers may vary. Possible response: There are rewards for making the right and honest choice.

Read the selection. Answer the questions that follow.

The Girl in the Maroon Robe

During the sixth grade, I constantly wore a maroon flannel robe. In fact, I wore it	16
so often it literally shredded one day in the washing machine. It wasn't particularly	30
attractive; it didn't even have pockets, but I loved it. It was comfortable and made	45
me feel secure.	48
Feeling secure was vital because I had low self-esteem. I was taller than all the	63
boys, skinny as a rail, and clumsy too. I was forever running into desks, causing	78
enormous bruises on my body. One day, I brought a chocolate cake to school	92
for Coach Marshall on Teacher Appreciation Day, but before I could deliver it, I	106
accidentally dropped the cake upside down in the hall. Everyone laughed, even	118
those who tried not to.	123
That was my sixth grade existence. I could accomplish nothing worthwhile.	134
Then one weekend day Mrs. Powers, a neighbor, stopped me at our mailbox. I was	149
enveloped in my maroon robe. She admitted she was concerned about me because	162
I looked so miserable. I wailed and explained how I felt. I felt hideous, and that I	179
couldn't do anything right. Mrs. Powers touched me on the shoulder. It felt like an	194
angel's hand rested there. Mrs. Powers said, "Laurie, you're a diamond in the rough.	208
One day you will shine brilliantly. Don't worry." Often remembering her words,	220
I've cherished them for decades.	225
I presume she recognized the value in me that I was too blind to see. Her	241
thoughtful words made me feel authentic, and I started thinking of myself as a	255
diamond—beautiful, strong, and shining.	260
As an award-winning writer today, I outshine my competition in every article I	273
pen, and I refuse to wear a flannel robe.	282

© Pearson Education 6

Turn the page.

Answer the questions below.

1 What event caused a positive change for the author?

   A entering the seventh grade

   B getting a maroon robe

   (C) Mrs. Powers' expression of concern

   D making a chocolate cake for Coach Marshall

2 The author refuses to wear a flannel robe today because

   F she has a silk one.

   (G) her writing success makes her feel secure.

   H her maroon robe was destroyed in the wash.

   J it can't replace her favorite one.

3 Based on the selection, what might be beneficial to all sixth graders?

   (A) having an adult believe in them

   B trying to stand out in the crowd

   C taking a cake to school

   D owning flannel robes

4 Why do you think the author wrote about her sixth-grade experience?

Answers may vary. Possible response: The author wanted to express hope to sixth graders who feel the same way and who might also be ready to discover their own strengths.

5 The author became an award-winning writer. What else does using her talent appear to have done for her?

Answers may vary. Possible response: Her talent for writing made her feel confident in her abilities in other aspects of her life.

Read the selection. Then answer the questions that follow.

Let's Get This Right

Gina showed up for school complaining to her friend Laura Mae about how	13
hectic things had been at her house the previous night. "I couldn't get the	27
geography assignment completed for Mrs. Lightner," she said, "so you've got to let	40
me copy what you did."	45
"Sorry," Laura Mae said, "I won't do that." Laura Mae's simple rule about	58
cheating was that she simply didn't do it.	66
"Look," Gina said, "either you help me out this one time, or we're no longer	81
friends."	82
Shocked by Gina's threat, Laura Mae stood silently by the school entrance,	94
thinking hard. She and Gina had been best friends for three years. "Let's discuss	108
this with Mrs. Lightner," she said. "I know she'll let you have another day if we	124
explain, and I promise to help you complete the work tonight."	135
Gina shook her head. It was *either/or*, she repeated. Either Laura Mae helped, or	150
the friendship was over.	154
"You're drawing the wrong conclusion," Laura Mae said with a frown. "This is	167
an *if/then* situation. If I let you bully me into cheating, then our friendship is over	184
for certain."	186

Turn the page.

Answer the questions below.

1 The "if/then" situation Laura Mae proposed tried to persuade

(A) Gina to make a choice between two things.

B Mrs. Lightner to go easy on Gina.

C someone to organize things at Gina's house.

D Gina to help her later with a future assignment.

2 How did Laura Mae respond to Gina's threat?

F She reported her to Mrs. Lightner.

G She let Gina copy her homework.

H She said their friendship was over.

(J) She suggested a different solution.

3 What happened just before Laura Mae explained her "if/then" conclusion?

A Mrs. Lightner gave the class a big assignment.

B Gina asked to copy Laura Mae's homework.

C Laura Mae refused to help Gina cheat.

(D) Gina repeated her threat a second time.

4 What or who does Gina seem to consider responsible for her not completing the geography assignment?

<u>Gina blames the hectic situation at her house the night</u>

<u>before.</u>

Read the selection. Then answer the questions that follow.

Looking Out for Lady

Marshall fed his dog Lady "Garden," a dog food advertised on TV as containing	14
vegetables, and one day he looked on the bag and realized there were practically	28
none in the product.	32
The next day at the pet mall, Marshall and Lady strolled along the aisles of dry	48
food. He leaned over bags of a brand name he recognized and ran his finger across	64
the information on it. A clerk wearing a green apron with "Primo" embroidered on	78
it explained, "Almost all of a food's content is covered by the first four ingredients	93
listed, and that product lists corn third under its ingredients."	103
"I like corn," Marshall acknowledged.	108
"Corn's difficult for dogs to digest," the man said, "so they don't get as much	123
nutrition from it as from a formula with rice. Corn's inexpensive to include and it	138
crowds out better ingredients."	142
"What do you recommend?" Marshall asked.	148
The man pointed at the name "Primo" on his apron. "No yellow corn in 'Primo,'"	163
he said, "and no animal by-products."	169
"Animal by-products sound unappetizing," Marshall agreed.	175
"They're food, but they don't provide a high-quality protein, while Primo Lamb	187
and Rice has the best ingredients you can feed this girl," he said, stooping to pet	203
Lady. The man added that Primo contained glucosamine and chondroitin "for	214
healthy joints" and that other ingredients would protect Lady's heart and maintain	227
her glossy coat. He pointed to each ingredient on a bag of Primo, which included,	241
he claimed, more of the healthful ingredients than other brands.	251
"How long have you worked for the store?" Marshall asked.	261
"I don't work for the store. I represent Primo," the man said.	273
Marshall became suspicious of the advice he was getting. He spent a half hour	287
comparing the ingredients of different dog food.	294
"There's a special now on Primo Lamb and Rice," the man said, passing by	308
again. "Each bag contains ten extra pounds, free."	316
Marshall acted like he faced a tough decision, then said, "I guess I'll try one	331
of those."	333

Turn the page.

Answer the questions below.

1 **What has the salesman concluded about corn?**

   A Dogs like corn more than other vegetables.

   B Corn provides better nutrition for dogs than rice does.

   (C) Some companies use corn because it is inexpensive.

   D Very little corn is used in most dog food.

2 **When Marshall goes to the pet mall to buy dog food, he has decided that he**

   F should buy a large bag of Primo dog food for Lady.

   G needs to talk to the Primo salesman.

   H knows enough about dog food ingredients.

   (J) wants to feed Lady something other than Garden.

3 **The salesman wants Marshall to conclude that Primo Lamb and Rice**

   A is a lot like most other dog food.

   B contains a lot of corn.

   (C) is better than all other dog food.

   D contains a lot of vegetables.

4 **What does Marshall conclude about the man in the green apron?**

   (F) He just wants to sell Marshall some Primo dog food.

   G He wants Marshall to have the best for Lady.

   H He actually works for the store.

   J He doesn't know much about dog food.

5 **Why does Marshall decide to buy Primo?**

Reading the dog food bags has not shown one brand to be superior, and the free ten pounds with a Primo purchase makes up his mind.

Read the selection. Then answer the questions that follow.

A Temporary Solution

Diego's Uncle Lucas gave odd birthday gifts. Sometimes, though, Diego thought	11
they were really cool. For example the time when Diego got a little portable CD	26
player with earphones made him think his Uncle Lucas was better than Santa Claus.	40
However, he was less enthusiastic the year he got a finger monitor to test his blood	56
pressure.	57
The story was that Uncle Lucas had once edited some kind of catalog for a big	73
store chain and then later for an Internet warehouse. We assumed that product	86
distributors had given those things to Lucas as gifts. When a holiday or birthday	100
came along, he wrapped one up, unused, and gave it as a gift.	113
The rule was never to reveal your disappointment if you got something peculiar	126
and to act grateful, even as if you had requested it. That worked tolerably well until	142
Diego unwrapped the label maker. It was fun at first. Diego typed in the name of	158
something and then stuck it on the object. "Notebook," Diego's notebook read.	170
Diego seemed very satisfied by naming things so plainly. Then he got carried	183
away and assumed the label maker would guarantee him an exceptionally	194
well-organized life. Labeling stuff became his obsession, and everything he	204
owned, he said, was going to have a label. You get a label maker from your kind	221
uncle, and you put your life in order.	229
"Stop, please!" I cried one afternoon as Diego labeled pieces of chalk with their	243
colors. He looked at me, realizing how ridiculous it all was. His face crinkled up,	258
and he started punching the keypad on that contraption like mad. Out came a long	273
piece of tape that Diego peeled and stuck across my shoulder. It read, "My helpful	288
amigo Carlos."	290
I was about to object when I noticed that the first labels Diego had put on things	307
were starting to peel off. The threat of the useful label maker would not last long.	323

© Pearson Education 6

Turn the page.

Answer the questions below.

1 According to the story, how did people believe Uncle Lucas selected the strange gifts he gave?

   A shopping in unusual catalogs

   B buying gifts on the Internet

   (**C**) choosing among free gifts he'd gotten

   D basing them on things people had requested

2 According to the speaker, Diego assumed that labeling all his things would help him

   F get work as a catalog editor.

   (**G**) put his things in good order.

   H show people how many things he had.

   J tell Uncle Lucas what kinds of things he needed.

3 What conclusion did Diego draw that the speaker disagreed with?

   A Uncle Lucas was a terrible shopper.

   (**B**) The label maker was a useful tool.

   C Uncle Lucas did not buy the gifts himself.

   D It was a good idea to act as if the gifts pleased you.

4 How is labeling Carlos the climax of the things Diego labeled?

The examples of what Diego labeled became more and more silly, and actually labeling a person made him realize just how much.

5 What does the title have to do with Diego's intention to label everything?

Diego's intention is to organize his life by labeling everything. This "solution" will be temporary because it only lasts as long as the labels do, which won't be long.

Read the selection. Then answer the questions that follow.

Letter to the Editor

I'm a seventh grader at Franklin Middle School, but I'll be saying good-by to	14
my old stomping grounds and to some of my good buddies next fall. I'm being	29
redistricted to go to Kenton, the new middle school.	38
I really love Franklin. I intended to run for Student Council President here, and	52
some of my best buddies will remain at this school.	62
But this school change had been scheduled from the day they started construction	75
on Kenton, which is just a few miles from where I live. Neighbors formed a	90
committee and protested. We requested that the School Board allow eighth graders	102
who are being redistricted to decide which school to attend. But the board did not	117
agree to our request.	121
Some parents and kids are still opposing redistricting, but I say it's time to move	136
on. I wanted to finish at Franklin, but I'll survive. I wish everyone facing this big	152
change would start looking for reasons it might be good for them.	164
—Ricky Alterado	166

© Pearson Education 6

Turn the page.

Answer the questions below.

1 Why won't Ricky be at Franklin Middle School next year?

   A They won't offer the grade he will be in.

   B Franklin Middle School is being torn down.

   (C) He is being sent to a different school.

   D He is moving to a different town.

2 If Ricky had gotten his way, what would have happened?

   F He would have started at Kenton this year.

   (G) The School Board would have let kids choose.

   H His parents would have been elected to the School Board.

   J He would have been President of the committee against redistricting.

3 Ricky's real reason for writing the newspaper was to

   A persuade people to fight redistricting students to new schools.

   B inform his friends that he wouldn't be attending Franklin next year.

   C brag about going to a brand new school.

   (D) suggest that parents and kids quit fighting redistricting and see its benefits.

4 What attitude about having to go to a new school is evident in Ricky's letter?

Ricky is making the best of what he cannot change, accepting the change, and trying to find reasons to look forward to it.

Read the selection. Then answer the questions that follow.

Let's Talk This Over One More Time!

Editorial

The Clanton County Commissioners recently voted to require billboards in our	1
	12
county to be moved farther away from the highway. They can be moved by the	
	27
owners of the property on which they stand, allowing them to retain the permit to	
	42
have a billboard. Or they can be moved by the billboard company, in effect giving	
	57
the company a new billboard permit.	
	63
Usually, the *Silvertown Bugle* would praise such an environment-enhancing	
	72
business decision. As the proponents of this ordinance change argued, good signage	
	84
is important to local businesses. It invites travelers to stop here, to spend some time	
	99
and support tourism. And signs, as it was also argued, are protected by freedom of	
	114
speech.	
	115
But the *Bugle* is very disappointed by this revision of our ordinance covering	
	128
billboards. It undoes the intention of the 1997 Commissioners, who decided that,	
	140
ultimately, Clanton County would be better off with *no* billboards blocking the	
	152
beautiful scenery that draws travelers here in the first place. That gentle law didn't	
	166
rush things. It said that there could be no *new* billboards and no *new* permits, but	
	182
standing billboards could remain standing until they wore out. The law forbade	
	194
upgrading these signs. They could be maintained, but not improved. They were to	
	207
go away through *attrition*—that is, to be removed when they became unstable.	
	220
The 1997 law has been thwarted by business interests ever since. First the courts	
	234
allowed the billboard company to "maintain" a billboard by rebuilding it completely	
	246
from the cement slab up. Now the Commissioners have allowed that billboards can	
	259
be moved and the permits for them retained or transferred.	
	269
This ordinance is a complete reversal of the intent of the 1997 Commissioners,	
	282
who clearly acted in response to a wide community sentiment. It is wrong to cast	
that intent aside without, at the very least, opening up the issue of billboards for	
renewed public discussion. Give people a chance to say whether they approve of the	
1997 law or want to undo it.	

© Pearson Education 6

Turn the page.

Answer the questions below.

1 The editorial suggests that the Commissioners changed the ordinance because

   A the newspaper argued that they should.

   (B) businesses pressured them to make the change.

   C the public decided that it liked having billboards.

   D travelers had complained about the absence of advertising.

2 The editorial starts out sounding like the *Bugle* wants

   (F) the Commissioners to change their mind.

   G the ordinance done away with permanently.

   H all billboards torn down right away.

   J the number of billboards to be doubled.

3 By the end of the editorial, what does the *Bugle* want done?

   A It wants the Commissioners voted out of office.

   B It wants people to fight for the rights of billboards.

   C It wants local businesses to decide about billboards.

   (D) It wants the whole county to have input on the new ordinance.

4 What seems to worry the editors of the *Bugle* most about the change in the billboard ordinance?

   F It will end up hiding all of the county's beautiful scenery.

   (G) It doesn't respect decisions that county leaders made earlier.

   H It gives the county businesses too much power.

   J It speeds up the removal of billboards in the county.

5 According to the author of the editorial, what was the first step courts took toward overriding the 1997 decision?

Courts allowed billboard maintenance to include rebuilding

from the slab up, which made the billboards newly stable.

Read the selection. Then answer the questions that follow.

Yesterday Comes Alive

Book Review

If you don't recognize the name Harriette Gillem Robinet, you're in for a great	2
read—a bunch of them! Robinet's novels present memorable young characters who	16
	28
live in history-making times and who experience mysteries and adventures of their	40
own. What you're always assured of from this productive author is an accurate	53
account of a historical setting and a really involving plot, with characters who	66
capture your heart and interest.	71

If you don't recognize the name Harriette Gillem Robinet, you're in for a great read—a bunch of them! Robinet's novels present memorable young characters who live in history-making times and who experience mysteries and adventures of their own. What you're always assured of from this productive author is an accurate account of a historical setting and a really involving plot, with characters who capture your heart and interest.

Robinet's novel *Twelve Travelers, Twenty Horses* begins on the eve of Lincoln's 1860 Presidential election on a courthouse square where slaves are being auctioned. At thirteen, Jacob has run away, has been recaptured, is put on sale again, and is purchased by a rich, young prospector, Clarence Higgenboom. They set out on the two-thousand-mile journey from Missouri to California, and Jacob becomes involved in rescuing the Pony Express from robbery. As in all of Robinet's novels, the reader gets a valuable perspective on a prime time in American history.

Robinet was born in Washington, D.C., and spent much of her childhood in Virginia. Her grandfather had been a slave there, in the household of Robert E. Lee. Robinet has graduate degrees in microbiology and now lives in Chicago. With her dozen novels, she has won a whole host of impressive awards.

Here are a few of her novels not to be missed—listed by their historic settings:

The War of 1812: In *Washington City Is Burning,* Virginia is a slave to President James Madison and his wife, Dolley.

Reconstruction times after the Civil War: In *Forty Acres and Maybe a Mule,* Nellie and her brother are slaves who run away with a friend from the Union Army to a new farm.

The Great Fire of Chicago: In *Children of the Fire,* Halleluia lives through the fire in 1871 and helps rebuild the city.

The Civil Rights Days of Rosa Parks: In *Walking the Bus Rider Blues,* Alfa and Zinnia solve a mystery while supporting the nonviolent bus boycott in Montgomery, Alabama.

Reviewed by Edward Passinger

	83
	95
	111
	123
	133
	147
	160
	173
	188
	201
	212
	228
	243
	249
	262
	278
	282
	296
	304
	318
	330
	332
	336

Turn the page.

- -

Answer the questions below.

1 One of Harriette Gillem Robinet's objectives as an author is to

　A　write about her ancestors.

　B　explain the field of microbiology.

　(C)　capture an important historic time.

　D　link all her novels together timewise.

2 It seems clear from the review that Robinet mainly wants to appeal to what reading audience?

　(F)　young people who like young characters and suspense

　G　high school teachers looking for novel assignments

　H　readers who enjoy stories about historic animals

　J　people fascinated by world history

3 Which of the following would be the best heading for a poster intended to advertise Robinet's books?

　A　"What Makes an Award-Winning Writer?"

　B　"One of Chicago's Most Talented Authors"

　(C)　"Visit Important Times in History!"

　D　"Have You Met Harriette Gillem Robinet?"

4 Why did Edward Passinger write this book review? Explain whether or not it is a favorable one and how that would affect readers.

Edward Passinger wrote the review to share his opinion of Robinet's works. He gave her a favorable review that would most likely spark the interests of its readers and perhaps encourage the audience to read Robinet's books.

5 Why does the author probably not discuss Robinet's academic area of study more?

Robinet studied microbiology, but microbiology does not appear to have anything to do with the material she writes about.

© Pearson Education 6

Read the selection. Then answer the questions that follow.

A Good Trade

As he walked home from school, Jeff's stomach growled. Lunch had been around	13
noon, and it was already four o'clock. Jeff passed several convenience stores but	26
had no money with him.	31
Then he saw the manager of the new health food store removing heavy cardboard	45
boxes from a van parked in the alley.	53
"Do you need some help?" Jeff asked.	60
"I sure do," the woman said, wiping her forehead. "Thanks for the offer."	73
Jeff jumped into the van and in fifteen minutes, with both of them working, two	88
dozen boxes of peanut butter were stacked in the store beside the bins of brown	103
rice.	104
Jeff was about to leave when the manager reached into a cooler and handed him a	120
sandwich and a cold bottle of juice. "I hope you like tuna, avocado, and sprouts on	136
whole wheat?" she said, reaching for a bottle of juice for herself.	148
"How did you know? It's my favorite," Jeff grinned.	157

Turn the page.

Answer the questions below.

1 Jeff's main problem as this story begins is that he is

   A sleepy.

   B angry.

   C hungry.

   D bored.

2 What happens when Jeff sees the woman unloading the truck?

   F He has to walk around the truck.

   G He asks for a job.

   H He drinks a bottle of juice.

   J He offers to help her.

3 Why does the woman give Jeff a sandwich?

   A because she feels sorry for him

   B because he asked for it

   C to try the new bread

   D as a reward for his work

4 Write three to five sentences to continue this story's plot. Write at least one line of dialogue.

Answers may vary. Possible responses: Jeff sat down, ate the sandwich, and drank the juice. The manager smiled at him. "If you come back tomorrow, I have another sandwich you can try." Jeff nodded, his mouth still full. Being helpful really paid off.

© Pearson Education 6

122

Fresh Reads Unit 5 Week 1 SI

Read the selection. Then answer the questions that follow.

The Gap

Evan, Martin, and Josh have their own band. Evan plays lead guitar, Martin plays	14
bass, and Josh sings. They take their music so seriously that they get together three	29
or four times a week and practice. They dream of performing at the local Youth	44
Center, but there's a gap. They need a drummer.	53
"My cousin plays drums," Martin offers after a very long practice.	64
"He also lives a hundred miles away," Josh groans. "Be real."	75
"Would you guys consider my sister Kate?" Evan suggests, packing up his guitar	88
and amplifier. "She's always begging to practice with us."	97
"I've seen your sister dance," Martin says. "She's got no rhythm at all!"	110
Evan admits this is true. Just because his sister learns most things quickly doesn't	124
mean she could learn to play drums.	131
The three musicians decide to post a notice on the bulletin board at the music	146
store downtown. It just announces, "Drummer Wanted," and includes Evan's phone	157
number. On Wednesday, when they post it, the three friends wonder if anyone will	171
call. By Sunday, Evan has received nine phone calls about the notice.	183
"I guess there are more drummers than we realized," Martin observes, studying	195
the list of names and phone numbers.	202
"Let's start calling," Josh says, grabbing the phone.	210
The boys call all nine drummers. Based on these conversations, they decide to	223
ask seven of them to audition. During the next two weeks, they spend practice time	238
with all seven, who have different skills and styles. Next, they ask three of them to	254
come back for another practice. The whole process takes nearly a month.	266
It's a hard choice, but their new band, called *The Gap,* has four members—	280
including a new drummer named Colleen—and a $400 gig at the Youth Center next	295
weekend.	296

Turn the page.

Answer the questions below.

1 Which sentence is the best summary of this story's plot?

(A) A band finds a drummer.

B Three musicians form a band.

C A band holds auditions.

D The Youth Center has a show.

2 What is the conflict faced by Evan, Martin, and Josh?

F They don't play very well.

G They can't find work.

H They can't hire Martin's cousin.

(J) They need another band member.

3 What happens after the boys hang up a notice?

A No one calls.

(B) Many people call.

C Evan's sister answers the ad.

D Only one person calls.

4 Which event is part of the rising action of the story?

F Josh becomes the lead singer.

(G) The boys hold auditions for drummers.

H Three boys decide to form a band.

J The Gap performs at the Youth Center.

5 Write two ways that the title is related to the plot of the story.

The lack of a drummer was a gap in the band, and the band's name became The Gap.

Read the selection. Then answer the questions that follow.

What a Waste

The Raymond Middle School Ecology Club meets every month. In September,	11
they choose a goal they work toward all year. This year, they chose "Improve the	26
practice of 'Reduce, Recycle, and Reuse' in our school cafeteria."	36
First, the club conducted a waste inventory. After a typical day, volunteers in	49
rubber gloves sorted the waste in the cafeteria garbage cans. It was a messy job,	64
but everyone laughed as they worked. The results were as follows: 13.5 pounds of	78
wasted food, 7.5 pounds of paper, 117 plastic utensils, 29 returnable glass bottles,	91
and 43 returnable cans.	95
Based on this study, club members estimated that in the 180 days of the school	110
year, the cafeteria generated more than a ton of wasted food. In addition, students	124
were throwing away more than $600 worth of returnable bottles and cans, about	137
21,000 plastic forks and spoons, and 1,350 pounds of recyclable paper.	148
To address this waste, the club built permanent recycling bins. Each one was	161
colorfully painted and clearly labeled so that no one would be confused about	174
where to throw trash. Daily, club members bagged returnable bottles and cans.	186
Weekly, the advisor and two volunteers returned them to a local redemption center.	199
Other volunteers bagged paper and delivered it to the town's recycling center. Still	212
others made connections with local farmers to collect waste food at the end of every	227
school day for both compost and animal feed.	235
In addition, the Ecology Club made a huge sign that explained the new system	249
to students and requested their participation. At the end of the year, Club members	263
agreed it was their best project ever. In addition to improving their school's	276
awareness and recycling more than two tons of waste, they raised more than $500	290
for next year's project.	294

Turn the page.

Answer the questions below.

1 **Which sentence is the best summary of this story's plot?**

  A The Raymond Middle School Ecology Club meets monthly.

  B The cafeteria generates more than a ton of waste food in a year.

  (C) An ecology club begins a recycling program in the school cafeteria.

  D Ecology clubs are set up in several communities.

2 **What happens first in this story?**

  (F) Club members do a waste inventory.

  G The Ecology Club raises more than $500.

  H The Ecology Club builds recycling bins.

  J Students throw away more than 21,000 plastic utensils.

3 **Why did the Ecology Club make a sign?**

  (A) to encourage students to recycle

  B to get more people to join the club

  C to raise money for the school

  D to set goals for the year

4 **How is the waste inventory important to the plot of this story?**

The waste inventory is important because it shows that there was a need for more recycling. It proves that a lot of food, paper, plastic, and returnables were being wasted in the school's cafeteria on a typical day.

5 **How does the author present the problem in this story?**

The problem presented in this story is the waste being generated in the school cafeteria. The author presents this problem in the title, "What a Waste," and then, in the second paragraph which contains specific details, in the form of statistics about this waste.

Read the selection. Then answer the questions that follow.

Yours Alone

Look at the tips of your fingers. Can you see the little ridges? These ridges,	15
called fingerprints, are yours alone. No two people have the same prints, and each	29
print leads to only one person. Also, fingerprints do not change throughout your	42
lifetime. For this reason, they are the most interesting part of your hands.	55
There are three types of fingerprints. Arch prints have straight lines from one	68
side of the finger to the other. Loop prints have lines that curve in a horseshoe turn.	85
In whorl prints, the lines make circles. Today, the FBI has more than two hundred	100
million prints on file. It is the largest collection in the world.	112
Police use fingerprints to catch criminals. A person leaves fingerprints on things	124
he or she touches. Police gather these prints by dusting things with chemicals that	138
make the prints visible. They take pictures of the prints and enlarge them. They	152
send the pictures to the FBI. Computers show whether they match any prints in the	167
FBI files. If they do, police can name that person without a doubt.	180
As you can see, fingerprints are a police officer's best tool.	191

Turn the page.

Answer the questions below.

1 Which of these is a statement of opinion about fingerprints?

   A Police use fingerprints to catch criminals.

   (B) Fingerprints are a police officer's best tool.

   C The FBI has more than two hundred million prints on file.

   D Arch prints have straight lines.

2 What does a police officer do first at a crime scene?

   (F) dusts objects for fingerprints

   G takes pictures of the fingerprints

   H sends the pictures to the FBI

   J waits to see whether the prints match any on file

3 Which of these sentences expresses the writer's opinion?

   A Fingerprints are yours alone.

   B No two people have the same fingerprint.

   C Fingerprints do not change throughout your lifetime.

   (D) Fingerprints are the most interesting part of your hands.

4 Is the following sentence a statement of fact or opinion? Give the reason for your answer.

   The first person to use fingerprints to identify people was William J. Hershel, a government official in India, in 1858.

   It is a statement of fact. It contains a specific name and date. I can look up this fact in an encyclopedia and discover whether it is true or false.

Read the selection. Then answer the questions that follow.

My Grandmother's Pearls

At special times, my grandmother wears a beautiful necklace made of about | 12
two dozen perfect white pearls. The last time I saw it, at my cousin's wedding, I | 28
decided to find out more about pearls and how they are made. What I discovered is | 44
a fascinating story. | 47

I was surprised to learn that pearls form inside the shells of oysters, the creatures | 62
that live on the ocean bottom. Unlike other gems that are dug from inside the | 77
Earth, these little beauties actually grow inside living ocean creatures! Oysters | 88
make a substance called *nacre* that lines the insides of their shells. When a foreign | 103
substance, such as a grain of sand, enters the body of an oyster, layers of nacre form | 120
on it. As time goes on, more and more layers grow. It takes years for that tiny grain | 138
to grow into a perfect pearl. | 144

To make a necklace like my grandmother's, you need many pearls of the same | 158
size and shape. Before the last century, divers found oysters and broke them open, | 172
hoping to discover pearls, a difficult task that needed both skill and luck. Most of | 187
the world's natural pearl beds are in the Persian Gulf. | 197

Since 1900, thanks to a Japanese inventor named Kokichi Mikimoto, people | 208
actually cultivate pearls. When young oysters are three years old, trained workers | 220
pry open their shells and insert tiny pellets made from mussel shells taken from the | 235
Mississippi River. The oysters are then lowered into the water in cages. Four years | 249
later, the oysters are opened. About one in every twenty oysters contains a perfect | 263
cultured pearl. | 265

About 70 percent of the world's cultured pearls are sold in the United States, just | 280
like the ones in my grandmother's beautiful necklace. | 288

Turn the page.

Answer the questions below.

1 Which of these is a statement of opinion about pearls?

   A About 70 percent of the world's cultured pearls are sold in the United States.

   B Kokichi Mikimoto invented cultured pearls.

   (C) Pearls are the most difficult gems to obtain.

   D It requires many layers of *nacre* to make a pearl.

2 What is the first step in making a cultured pearl?

   F Insert a tiny pellet from a mussel shell.

   G Lower the oyster back into the water.

   H Open the oyster and look for a pearl.

   (J) Collect an oyster that is three years old.

3 Which of these sentences appears to express the speaker's opinion?

   A My grandmother owns a pearl necklace.

   (B) The story of how pearls are made is fascinating.

   C Most of the world's natural pearls come from the Persian Gulf.

   D Pearls grow in the shells of ocean creatures.

4 What is the best way to verify the fact that pearls can be black, white, pink, or orange.

   F Ask the person who wrote this selection.

   (G) Research pearls in a library or online.

   H Go to a jewelry store and look at pearls.

   J Look inside an oyster.

5 Is the following sentence a statement of fact or opinion? Give the reason for your answer.
Kokichi Mikimoto has been the most successful inventor in the history of Japan.

This sentence is a statement of opinion. Whether Mikimoto was successful or not might be considered factual, but whether he is "most" successful cannot be proved because it depends on how success is measured.

© Pearson Education 6

Read the selection. Then answer the questions that follow.

The History of Paper
by Sarah Roosevelt

Paper is the most important invention in human history. Without it, there	12
would be no books, letters, documents, or records. Without it, there would be no	26
governments, history, or financial systems.	31
More than five thousand years ago, the Egyptians made a writing material from a	45
plant called *papyrus*, from which the word *paper* derives. They cut these reeds into	59
thin slices and then pressed them together into long scrolls. About 2000 B.C., the	73
Egyptians replaced the scrolls with sheets that they bound together, much like our	86
modern books.	88
What we think of as paper was invented by the Chinese in A.D. 105 by a	104
government minister of public works named Ts'ai Lun. He discovered that the inner	117
bark of the mulberry tree could be broken into fibers and pounded into a flat sheet.	133
Based on this method, the Chinese also made paper out of rags, hemp, and even old	149
fishnets.	150
The art of making paper spread from China to the Middle East. When Europeans	164
came to Northern Africa and Spain, papermaking spread north. For several hundred	176
years, paper was made by hand from rag pulp, but in 1798 this changed. Frenchman	191
Nicholas Louis Robert invented a machine that made paper from wood pulp in	204
long continuous rolls rather than in small batches. His invention set the stage for	218
newspapers.	219
In 1840 a German named Friedrich Keller invented a process for grinding logs	232
into pulp, and later chemists added sulfurous acid to the wood as a preservative.	246
Today, most of the world's paper is made in the United States from pulp from	261
spruce, fir, hemlock, and pine trees found in the northern United States and Canada.	275
Even in this computer age, it is difficult to imagine a world—or even a day—	291
without paper.	293

Turn the page.

© Pearson Education 6

Answer the questions below.

1 How does the writer begin this selection?

   A She begins with specific facts about paper's popularity.

   (B) She offers an opinion about the importance of paper.

   C She describes how paper is made.

   D She tells a story of how paper was invented.

2 Who invented paper as we know it?

   F Friedrich Keller in Germany

   G Nicholas Robert in France

   (H) Ts'ai Lun in China

   J chemists in the United States

3 Which of these sentences appears to express the writer's opinion?

   A The word *paper* comes from the word *papyrus*.

   B Today, most of the world's paper is made in the United States.

   C Papermaking spread from China to the Middle East.

   (D) It's difficult to imagine a world without paper.

4 Is the following sentence a statement of fact or a statement of opinion? Give the reason for your answer.

   In A.D. 105, Ts'ai Lun made paper from the inner bark of the mulberry tree.

   This sentence is a statement of fact. It includes a date, a specific name, and an event from history that can be proved true.

5 Can you tell what the writer's opinion is about recycling paper? Explain your answer.

   No. The writer says that paper in the United States is made of different trees but does not use any clue words suggesting whether that is good or bad. The writer does not mention recycling at all.

Read the selection. Then answer the questions that follow.

Darkness Wins

The math team met at 7:00 P.M. one evening to prepare for an upcoming	14
tournament.	15
Michael and Susan arrived early. They spread their notebooks, practice tests, and	27
calculators all over the table. Steven and Erica showed up soon and spread out	41
their notes from the last three meets. When Ms. Donnelly, their advisor, arrived at	55
7:00 P.M., they had already started planning how they might best spend the next	69
two hours.	71
At 7:05, all the lights went out and everyone groaned. "Let's wait a few minutes,"	86
Ms. Donnelly suggested, "and maybe the electricity will come back on."	97
They waited ten minutes, then fifteen. At 7:30, they agreed that it was foolish	111
to sit in the dark. They groped around the table, searching for books, backpacks,	125
pencils, calculators, and papers. They kept bumping into each other, laughing and	137
saying "Excuse me." At 7:45, when Ms. Donnelly closed the heavy classroom door,	150
the loud click echoed in the empty hallway.	158
Just as they stepped outside, the lights came on. Everyone laughed. "Should we	171
go back in?" the students asked.	177
"No," Ms. Donnelly sighed. "I've had a long day. Tonight, the darkness won."	190

Turn the page.

Answer the questions below.

1 Why did the students pack up all their materials and leave the school?

   A They were to have a math tournament soon.

   B The electricity came back on.

   C The electricity failed and it was too dark to see.

   D Their adviser told them they didn't need to practice.

2 To show the sequence of events in this story, the writer used

   F a third person point of view.

   G a school as the setting for the story.

   H a series of times from 7:00 to 7:45.

   J everyone's names in the second paragraph.

3 Why did Ms. Donnelly decide not to return to the classroom?

   A Everyone was groaning and complaining.

   B Donna had notes from three other meets.

   C No one could see to practice.

   D She was tired and ready to go home.

4 Will the electricity going out probably have a positive or negative effect on the math team's performance in the tournament? Explain your answer.

The electricity going out will probably have a negative effect on the math team's performance in the tournament because they did not have the two hours of preparation they had planned.

Name _____

Read the selection. Then answer the questions that follow.

A New Land

Greta watched Peter, her younger brother, spread the freshly-cut hay with a	12
wooden rake. They were following their two older brothers who were cutting hay	25
several yards ahead. Walking ahead of Peter, Greta steadily turned the long line	38
of hay with a pitchfork. Together they made certain that the fresh hay was spread	53
evenly. They made sure not to leave clumps of damp hay that might get moldy. In	69
a few days, when the hay had dried in the sun thoroughly, they would gather it into	86
shocks, or bundles.	89
Greta was thinking about the journey that she and her family had made two years	104
ago in 1868.	107
"Do you realize, Peter," said Greta, "that there are almost three million German	120
people who have immigrated to America?"	126
"Did they all settle here in Pennsylvania?" asked Peter.	135
"No," replied Greta. "Many Germans who came to America ten years ago settled	148
in Illinois and Ohio."	152
Greta waited as Peter raked another row of hay. "Why did so many Germans	166
come to America?" he asked.	171
"Not enough jobs existed in Germany," responded Greta. "As a result, many	183
people were unemployed. In America, people were able to find work. Many of the	197
Germans who immigrated to this country settled in Pennsylvania and the Midwest."	209
"In these states," Greta continued, "the land is rich and good for growing crops.	223
Furthermore, much of the land is available for farming."	232
Greta and Peter spread more hay to dry. Greta knew that when the hay was all	248
dry, binding it into bundles would make it easier to handle. In a few days, her	264
brothers would gather the bundles and stack them in the barn.	275
"When winter comes," said Peter, "I think the animals will be happy that they	289
have all this hay to eat . . . as happy as we are to be in America."	304

Turn the page.

© Pearson Education 6

Answer the questions below.

1 What caused so many German people to immigrate to the United States during the 1850s?

   A There was an epidemic of influenza in Germany.

   B There were not enough jobs in Germany.

   C They had heard that gold had been discovered in California.

   D They were fleeing religious persecution.

2 Why did German farmers settle in Pennsylvania and the Midwest states?

   F The Mississippi river would help them get their crops to market.

   G They came to join family members.

   H The land there was rich and good for growing crops.

   I They could trade with Native Americans for food.

3 Why were Greta and Peter spreading the cut hay?

   A to fertilize the soil

   B to protect young plants from the cold

   C to prepare the land for plowing

   D so that it would dry in the sun

4 Why will Greta's brothers stack the dried hay in the barn?

   F The stored hay will feed the farm animals over the winter.

   G The hay will protect the animals from the cold.

   H The seeds from the hay will grow next year's crop.

   I To sell to farmers in the winter when feed is scarce.

5 How might you present information about German immigration to the United States in a graphic organizer?

I could make a time line showing how many immigrants arrived and in what years.

Name _____

Read the selection. Then answer the questions that follow.

How Iron Is Mined

The most abundant metal on Earth, iron, exists in every state in the United States	15
and nearly every country on the planet. Every day, miners extract thousands of	28
tons of iron so humans can manufacture tools, buildings, machines, gadgets, and	40
furniture. Today, mining companies use two methods to extract iron ore from the	53
earth: open pit mining and tunnel mining.	60
Most of the world's iron ore and 96 percent of the ore mined in the United States	77
are extracted by *open pit mining*. As you travel on highways across the United	91
States, you might notice these gaping pits, sometimes carved into the sides of	104
mountains. To many environmentalists, these open pits resemble ugly open wounds.	115
To create an open pit mine, miners first strip away several feet of surface layer with	131
enormous excavation machines, and then they use explosives to loosen and shatter	143
chunks of ore. Enormous power shovels scoop the ore into railroad hopper cars	156
that transport it to mills for processing. The largest open pit mine in the world is	172
the Hull-Rust-Mahoning mine near Hibbing, Minnesota, which is three-and-a-half	181
miles long and more than 350 feet deep. Open pit mines such as this supply about	197
85 percent of the iron ore used in the United States.	208
Tunnel mining, or shaft mining, is necessary when the ore deposits are deeper	221
underground. Miners dig tunnels straight into the deposit and then descend into	233
them to remove the ore. Often, secondary tunnels branch from the main shaft.	246
Mining companies install conveyor belts, elevators, or special railroad cars to move	258
the ore to the surface for transportation. Sometimes, miners drill tunnel mines	270
horizontally into the slopes of mountains. Because tunnel mining is more hazardous	282
and expensive than open pit mining, it is used only when there's a rich, vast deposit	298
of top-quality ore.	302

© Pearson Education 6

Turn the page.

Answer the questions below.

1 One effect of an open pit mine is that it creates

A ugly raw areas on the land.

B underground railroads.

C smaller mines.

D mines that are less likely to be seen.

2 Why do miners use tunnel mining rather than open pit mining?

F Tunnel mining is less expensive than open pit mining.

G Tunnel mining reaches iron too deep to mine from open pits.

H Tunnel mining is much safer than open pit mining.

J Tunnel mining takes much less time than open pit mining.

3 Which of these steps occurs first in open pit mining?

A Explosives loosen the ore.

B Shovels scoop the ore into trucks.

C Huge machines scrape away the top layer of dirt.

D The ore is transported to iron mills.

4 Why are open pit mines probably very loud?

Huge machines and explosives are used to loosen iron ore from the earth.

5 If the Hull-Rust-Mahoning mine were to be made larger, would it probably be made deeper or longer? Explain your answer.

It would probably be made longer. It is probably already as deep as it needs to be.

Read the selection. Then answer the questions that follow.

Two Kinds of Terns

Terns are huge sea birds, well-known for their powers of flight. Their wingspan	13
can reach more than four feet. As terns fly, they dive into the sea to catch fish. Two	31
kinds of terns live on Earth: Arctic terns live at the North Pole and Antarctic terns	47
live near the South Pole.	52
Antarctic terns dig holes in the bare Earth in October. Their eggs are brown	66
and tan like the sand around them. The parents fly to and from the nest, returning	82
with fish for their young. Antarctic terns breed in Antarctica during the summer	95
(November to January) and then fly to warmer seas near South America during the	109
winter (June to August).	113
Their northern cousin, the Arctic tern, breeds near the North Pole in the summer	127
(June to August) and then flies all the way south to the Antarctic to enjoy *another*	143
summer from November to January! They fly over fifteen thousand miles, farther	155
than any other bird. On their southern vacation, Arctic terns feed at sea before	169
returning north in March.	173
They may look alike, but the two kinds of terns mate in different parts of the	189
year, at different poles, and only with others like themselves.	199

Turn the page.

Answer the questions below.

1 **What is the main idea of this selection?**
- **(A)** The two kinds of terns are similar but different.
- **B** Terns are huge sea birds.
- **C** Terns are in danger of becoming extinct.
- **D** Arctic terns and Antarctic terns are the same birds.

2 **Which of the following true statements supports the main idea?**
- **F** Scientists who study birds are called ornithologists.
- **G** Very few animals live in Antarctica.
- **(H)** Both types of terns are brown and have broad wings.
- **J** At the South Pole, winter lasts from November to January.

3 **The selection indicates that terns**
- **A** are very shy birds.
- **(B)** have amazing powers of flight.
- **C** only live at the South Pole.
- **D** only eat plants.

4 **What would be a probable effect if an Arctic tern did not fly south in September or October?**

Answers may vary. Possible response: It might not survive the cold of Arctic winter. It might not find enough food to eat during the winter.

Read the selection. Then answer the questions that follow.

A New Kind of Writing

Louis Braille was born in 1809 in the village of Coupvray near Paris, France. His	15
father made shoes and harnesses. As a child, Louis was playing with an awl in his	31
father's workshop when it slipped and damaged one eye, permanently blinding it.	43

By the time he was four, the sight in Braille's other eye was damaged by | 58
infection, and the boy lost his sight completely. However, he showed great promise | 71
in school, especially in music, and was enrolled in the Royal Institution for the | 85
Blind in Paris. He learned to read by feeling raised print on paper, the most popular | 101
system at the time. This reading went very slowly, however, because it was difficult | 115
to tell the letters apart by touch. This method also didn't offer a way for blind | 131
people to write. | 134

In 1821, Louis Braille learned about a new kind of writing developed for the | 148
French military called "night writing." It used a system of twelve raised dots in | 162
various patterns to represent certain sounds. Braille saw a great possibility for the | 175
use of this system for the blind, and spent the next few years experimenting with | 190
it and simplifying it. The system he invented used just six dots, first for words and | 206
letters and later for math and music. | 213

The first book in Braille was published in 1829, but the system didn't catch | 227
on for a very long time. When Louis Braille died in 1852, the magnitude of his | 243
achievement hadn't yet been recognized, and the system he invented wasn't widely | 255
known. Today, Braille is used all over the world in almost every language on the | 270
planet, and the man who invented it is honored as a great hero of France and one of | 288
the world's great inventors. | 292

Turn the page.

Answer the questions below.

1 The main idea of the second paragraph is

(A) Braille learned to read letters by touch.

B Braille lost his sight in an accident.

C Braille invented a new kind of writing.

D Braille went to school in Paris.

2 Which of the following details does not support the idea that the system used at the Royal Academy could be improved?

F The letters could not be used to write.

G Many letters felt alike.

H Reading went very slowly.

(J) The alphabet was already familiar.

3 The last paragraph supports the idea that

A Braille is one of the only inventors to become a hero.

B It took more than twenty-five years for the Braille system to catch on.

(C) Braille's achievement had a far-reaching global impact.

D Nearly everyone in the world can read Braille.

4 Which of the following expresses a broad main idea of this selection?

F Using Braille is good for everyone, blind or not.

(G) Physical impairments can lead to great inventions.

H Many people lose their eyesight because of infection.

J The French military, not Louis Braille, invented this new kind of language.

5 Why was the military system of raised letters probably called "night writing"?

This system was probably called "night writing" because soldiers could read it even in the dark. To read it, they used their sense of touch rather than their sense of sight.

Read the selection. Then answer the questions that follow.

A Gem of a Park

Crystal Lake Park in Harrison is a gem. The first thing you see is two sets of | 17

green painted bleachers overlooking a softball field. In the spring, you'll see boys | 30

and/or girls learning to pitch or adults enjoying a game of softball. Nearby, a | 44

basketball court holds ramps used by local skateboarders and BMX bikers. The | 56

"Food Booth" sells popcorn, hot dogs, candy, and soft drinks. Children swing, slide, | 69

and climb on new playground equipment. A dozen picnic tables, each with its own | 83

grill, hide among clumps of birches. The park's most dramatic feature is the clean, | 97

gently sloping beach, full of grandparents under umbrellas and toddlers with plastic | 109

buckets. On hot summer days, the parking lot is always full. | 120

Crystal Lake Park originated in 1972, when voters approved funds to turn the | 133

Victorian Hunt Manor into a park. The property had been purchased by the town in | 148

1968. Most of the construction took place during 1973. In 1982, the Harrison Men's | 162

Club held a fundraising drive to build and fence a basketball court at the park. | 177

With help from the Lions Club and lots of volunteer labor, the town erected its own | 193

hoops. In July of 1983, Ken Stackpole donated a new scoreboard. In 1985, the Old | 208

Home Days Committee voted to construct the wooden booth at the park. In 1987, | 222

the Crystal Lake boat ramp was proposed. It was completed in November of 1989. | 236

In 1999, most of the park's old metal playground equipment was declared unsafe | 249

and removed. The Playground Committee formed and began to raise money and | 261

draw plans. Through the generous support of Harrison taxpayers, businesses, and | 272

organizations, $41,000 was raised. In May and September of 2000, community | 283

volunteers built a new modern playground that will be safe for many years to come. | 298

© Pearson Education 6

Turn the page.

Answer the questions below.

1 You might expect to find this selection in a
  A textbook about lakes and rivers.
  (B) history of Harrison.
  C brochure about the Victoria Hunt Manor.
  D letter from the Playground Committee to local businesses.

2 Which of the following activities is not mentioned as being available in Crystal Lake Park?
  F softball
  G cookouts
  H swimming
  (J) tennis

3 Why did the town decide to build a new playground?
  A A flood had damaged the old playground.
  B The site of the old playgound was too uneven.
  (C) The old playground equipment was no longer safe.
  D Everyone preferred the look of more modern equipment.

4 What about the park's location makes it more special than a park in the middle of town?

__The park is next to a lake, which allows for more activities__
__and a nice view.__

5 Given that the old playground equipment was probably in the park from 1973 to 1999, what might some children have in common with their parents?

__They played on exactly the same playground equipment as__
__their parents did when they were children.__

Read the selection. Then answer the questions that follow.

Math?

I hadn't worked as a substitute teacher in years when I was asked to fill in for Mr.	18
Grasso, a math teacher.	22
First period was slow and quiet. From 7:30 until 8:45, fifteen calculus students	35
worked diligently. Two or three of them sipped coffee, and one ate a granola bar.	50
Second period was more lively. Tenth graders struggled with an Algebra One test.	63
"Didn't Mr. Grasso cancel this test?" a tall boy said hopefully.	74
"Nice try," I said.	78
Third period I had lunch duty: loud, smelly, and sticky.	88
Fourth period was Freshman Math, and as students sat using their calculators	100
for an assignment, one girl in the back kept making noises at hers—little whistling	115
sounds.	116
"Excuse me," I said, walking over. "Please don't talk to your calculator."	128
Everyone burst into laughter.	132
"It's not a calculator," she said sheepishly. "It's a toy, a computerized game." She	146
handed it to me. I'm afraid I borrowed it for the rest of the class, and made some	164
whistling sounds of my own.	169

Turn the page.

- -

Answer the questions below.

1 What clue words in the story showed the sequence of events?

(A) first, second, third, fourth

B calculus, algebra, freshmen

C and, so, or, but

D morning, afternoon, evening, night

2 Which of these events happened first in the story?

(F) A student ate a granola bar.

G An algebra class took a test.

H The speaker had lunch duty.

J The speaker played computer games.

3 This story mostly took place

A in a teacher's lounge.

B in a gymnasium.

C in the speaker's living room.

(D) in a math class.

4 Based on the story, what did the speaker probably do with the student's "calculator" after class?

He probably returned the "calculator" to the student.

Read the selection. Then answer the questions that follow.

The Night the Stars Fell

Once upon a time, a cat named Lance was enjoying his usual walk after sunset	15
and noticed his friend Moon peeking over the horizon. Lance tiptoed through	27
clusters of pine trees, stopped to ponder, and spotted the most dramatic sight he had	42
ever witnessed: a star that twinkled as brightly as a diamond suspended in space.	56
"I admit," Lance exclaimed to Moon, "that if I could play with that twinkling	70
star, I'd be the most grateful cat alive!" Lance had once played with a grasshopper	85
for an entire afternoon, which had, until tonight, been his happiest experience. Lance	98
climbed a tree and perched on its uppermost branch, staring at the star as he did.	114
Moon observed his friend and chuckled, "What are you going to do, wait for it to	130
fall?"	131
"Exactly," Lance answered, very certain of himself.	138
"Stars don't fall," Moon announced, just as certain, "and you are an extremely	151
foolish cat."	153
Ignoring his doubtful friend and gluing his enormous yellow eyes on the April	166
sky as it blackened, Lance repeated his wish, over and over, that the star would fall.	182
During the darkest hour of midnight, Lance's eyelids grew heavier and heavier, and	195
finally he fell into a deep kitty sleep. The sky turned the color of a budding rose as	213
Lance dreamed about batting that star around in the woods.	223
When Lance awoke to chirping chickadees, he was amazed at the spectacle	235
surrounding him. Stars twinkled everywhere: on the boulders, on the branches, on	247
the buds, and on the webs that the spiders had woven in the night.	261
"It's only dew, you foolish cat," grumbled Moon as he settled in for his daily	276
snooze, but Lance knew not only that his wish had come true, but also that the star	293
had burst into a million stars, each one for his particular delight.	305

© Pearson Education 6

Turn the page.

- -

Answer the questions below.

1 Where and when did the story take place?

   A   on a weekend in a neighborhood

   (B)   in the woods in April

   C   in a very tall tree at dawn

   D   on a starry night in January

2 Which of these events happened first in the narrative?

   F   The sun set.

   (G)   Lance saw a bright star.

   H   Lance saw stars everywhere.

   J   Moon and Lance had a conversation.

3 Which of these phrases is a clue that shows chronological order?

   A   as brightly as a diamond ring

   (B)   after some hours had passed

   C   staring at the star as he did

   D   each one for his particular delight

4 Which of these is a brief flashback in this narrative?

   F   another of Lance's usual walks

   G   the sky turning the color of a budding rose

   H   dew falling from the sky at dawn

   (J)   Lance playing with a grasshopper

5 This story's beginning, middle, and end happen at three corresponding times of day. What are those times? Identify them in the order they appear in the story.

The story begins around sunset. The middle of the story is around midnight, and the story ends at dawn.

Read the selection. Then answer the questions that follow.

The Penny Drive

On Friday afternoon in Mr. Adams's social studies class, everyone was anxious	12
for the weekend. "Only one more assignment," Mr. Adams announced, trying to	24
sound upbeat. "We've been challenged to raise $100 to support the library fund, and	38
we only have a week, so let's brainstorm possibilities."	47
"We could organize a bake sale," Cassandra chirped from the front row, always	60
ready for dessert.	63
"In case you haven't noticed," Tom moaned, "we're not in elementary school	75
anymore."	76
"We could hold a car wash," Carl said, always interested in cars.	88
"It's January, Carl," Mr. Adams reminded him, "and it's freezing outside."	99
In the back row, Mark dozed, and as he stared at a copper spot on the floor,	116
Abraham Lincoln stared back. When Mark thought aloud, "How about a penny	128
drive?" no one objected. As the bell rang, Mr. Adams called, "This weekend, collect	142
as many pennies as possible!"	147
On Monday, Danny brought his grandmother's penny collection: more than 1,200	158
pennies. Others brought pocketfuls and handfuls, and at the end of the day, they'd	172
rolled $27.58. On Tuesday, Mr. Adams brought in 499 pennies, the school secretary	185
contributed 963 from a jar in her kitchen, and others donated 497. On Wednesday,	199
the librarian donated 285 and the principal, 227. Over the weekend, Darcy had put	213
a jar in the grocery store with a sign explaining the project, and customers donated	228
896 pennies in four days.	233
On Friday, dozens of students from the entire school brought jars, envelopes,	245
boxes, plastic and paper bags, and even an orange juice can full of pennies. The	260
class rolled another 3,862, which pushed their total to $99.87. "Wow," Mr. Adams	273
admitted, "and thanks for the proposal, Mark. Perhaps you have a future in	286
finance!"	287
From the back row, Mark grinned, picturing himself behind an enormous	298
mahogany desk, the president of an international bank.	306

© Pearson Education 6

Turn the page.

Answer the questions below.

1 Which of these are "clue words" that signal chronological order in this selection?

A Friday, Monday, Tuesday, Wednesday, Friday

B January, February, March, April

C in the front row, in the back row

D Cassandra, Tom, Carl, and Mark

2 Which event happened last in the story?

F Darcy put a jar and a sign in the local grocery store.

G Mark imagined himself a banker.

H Carl suggested that they hold a car wash.

J Mr. Adams thanked Mark for the proposal.

3 If the story were to continue, which of the following would be the most logical event?

A Mr. Adams quit his teaching job and became a banker.

B All the pennies were returned to their donators.

C The class presented a $100 check to the library fund.

D The class decided to hold a nickel drive.

4 Consider the students' ideas for raising money. From what two general sources do their ideas come?

Their ideas come from what they themselves like (baked goods and cars) and from what they see around them (a penny).

5 Although the actual setting of the story is a social studies class, what two other settings, as sources of pennies, are mentioned?

The secretary's kitchen and the grocery store are also mentioned.

Read the selection. Then answer the questions that follow.

The Smallest Poems

Haiku (hi-koo) are very small poems. They were invented by Japanese poets | 12

in the sixteenth century. These little poems, only three lines long, have seventeen | 25

syllables. There are five syllables in the first line, seven in the second line, and five | 41

again in the third line. | 46

Haiku are about single moments of experience. They are often about nature or | 59

the seasons. The best ones offer surprise and delight to their readers. Here are three | 74

modern haiku: | 76

A full moon tonight: | 80

I will howl! I will hunt in | 87

the woods with the owl. | 92

The cat's face: wise with | 97

two golden mirrors like her | 102

cup and saucer eyes. | 106

The last of the snow | 111

slides off the metal roof: Spring | 117

swallowing Winter. | 119

The next time you see something in the world that gets your attention, try | 133

expressing it in a haiku. They are as much fun to write as they are to read. | 150

Turn the page.

Answer the questions below.

1 Why did the author include three haiku?

  A to make her readers laugh out loud

  B to share her feelings about her pets

  C to get the reader's attention

  (D) to show examples of what haiku can be about

2 In the first two paragraphs, the author

  F shares Japanese history.

  (G) defines and explains haiku.

  H compares cats and cups.

  J discusses several different kinds of poems.

3 In the last paragraph, the author

  A explains that haiku are too difficult for most people to write.

  B claims that no one writes haiku anymore.

  (C) encourages the reader to try writing haiku.

  D notes that haiku should always be read aloud.

4 In which, if any, of the three haiku is the author's presence evident? Explain your answer.

The author's presence is evident only in the first haiku, where the pronoun "I" is used.

Read the selection. Then answer the questions that follow.

Noah Webster's Spelling Book

Noah Webster was born in 1758. He grew up on a small farm in Connecticut, and | 16
after attending college he became a lawyer. He didn't practice for long, however. | 29
He started teaching and went on to become one of the most famous of all American | 45
educators. | 46

Noah loved working with words, and he came to the conclusion that a good | 60
spelling book would do more to spread the English language across the nation than | 74
any other type of book. | 79

At first, spelling in English was irregular. Words did not have a single correct | 93
spelling, as they do today. People could, and did, spell the same words in many | 108
different ways. A document from the Massachusetts court system in 1646 spelled | 120
the word "eternal" this way: "aetaernall." | 126

As time passed, spelling became more regular. But many people still used the | 139
British spellings of some words. For example, the words "center" and "honor" | 151
were often spelled "centre" and "honour." | 157

Noah Webster changed all this and argued that Americans needed their own | 169
simpler and more regular spelling. His book aimed to provide just that. | 181

Noah's speller was called *The American Spelling Book,* and it was published | 193
in 1783. It showed the pronunciation of words and gave spellings that reflected | 206
the way the words were pronounced. Later, Noah added pictures and fables as | 219
well. He also wrote a grammar book, a reading book, and a dictionary that further | 234
standardized English spelling. | 237

Even Noah was surprised at the popularity of his spelling book. Soon the speller | 251
could be found in homes and schools throughout the states. Because of the book, | 265
contests called spelling bees became popular. They were often held in schoolrooms, and | 278
were attended by young and old alike. However, the most important effect the speller | 292
had was to establish a standard in the United States for spelling and pronouncing words. | 307

Turn the page.

© Pearson Education 6

- -

Answer the questions below.

1 1. In the selection the writer compares

    A good writing with bad writing.

    B the popularity of Webster's speller with that of other kinds of books.

    (C) American spellings and British spellings of some words.

    D American writing and British writing.

2 The author of the selection assumes that the reader

    F has studied Noah Webster.

    (G) is interested in American history.

    H has heard about Webster's speller.

    J is a writer.

3 The author's purpose in writing this selection seems to be

    A to explore the possibility of writing a new spelling book.

    B to inspire the reader to be a better speller.

    (C) to tell the reader about an interesting part of American history.

    D to become a spelling teacher.

4 Throughout the selection the author

    F seems critical and sarcastic about spelling books.

    G encourages readers to use a standardized spelling system.

    H used a very relaxed and informal tone.

    (J) is factual and informative.

5 What did you learn about Noah Webster's effect on American education?

Webster helped to standardize English spelling. Spelling bees became popular and were held in schools.

Read the selection. Then answer the questions that follow.

Ski Black Hawk Mountain

In 1955, Black Hawk Mountain, just east of Middleton, opened its 230 | 12

breathtaking acres as a ski area. In operation ever since, this 2,100-foot peak with | 26

1,900 feet of vertical drop offers thirty-four day trails and twelve night trails. We're | 40

open 9 A.M. to 9 P.M. on Mondays through Thursdays, 9 A.M. to 10 P.M. on Fridays | 57

and Saturdays, and 9 A.M. to 4 P.M. on Sundays. Thirty percent of the trails are for | 74

beginners. Forty-five percent are for intermediate skiers, and twenty-five percent are | 85

for experts. New this winter is a half-pipe for snowboarders. | 95

Skiing at Black Hawk Mountain won't break the bank. For only $30, an adult can | 110

ski all day and into the evening. Students and seniors ski for $20, and kids under six | 127

ski free. It's a great way for the whole family to spend a winter day. | 142

For food service, the mountain offers The Igloo, which serves sandwiches, salads, | 154

and soups, and the Snackpack, which offers hot drinks, pizza, candy, and snacks. | 167

Many skiers bring their own food and take breaks in the roomy Time Out Lounge | 182

full of picnic tables. Lockers are available in a room nearby at $5 per day. | 197

Taking a lesson is the most successful way to learn to ski. Certified and | 211

experienced instructors teach group classes of no more than a dozen students at ten, | 225

one, and three o'clock daily. Private lessons are available whenever the mountain is | 238

open. Group lessons are $15; private lessons are $30 per hour. | 249

If you want to ski for several days, consider booking a suite or a room at the | 266

Black Hawk Inn, only a short hike from the base lodge. Its huge stone fireplace is | 282

a gathering spot for tired feet, and each room has bunk beds and trundle beds to | 298

accommodate families and groups. Rates vary, so call the manager for information. | 310

If you love to ski . . . or if you *want* to ski . . . Black Hawk Mountain is the | 332

perfect spot for your winter vacation. | 338

Turn the page.

Answer the questions below.

1 In the first paragraph, the author

   A persuaded the reader to take a ski lesson.

   B gave directions to Black Hawk Mountain.

   (C) described the ski mountain, its trails, and its hours.

   D suggested that snowboarding is easier than skiing.

2 In paragraphs 2 through 5, the author provided information about

   F why night skiing is more fun than day skiing.

   G lockers, tables, snacks, and salads.

   H fireplaces in the Black Hawk Inn.

   (J) costs, food, lessons, and lodging.

3 In the last paragraph, the author's purpose is to

   A inform readers about their choices at Black Hawk Mountain.

   (B) persuade readers to ski at Black Hawk Mountain.

   C show readers how much money they can save at Black Hawk Mountain.

   D convince readers to eat at The Igloo.

4 Based on the selection, does the author appear to be a visitor reviewing the ski resort as a vacation spot, or a person who works at the ski resort? Explain your answer.

The author appears to be a person who works at the ski resort. My answer is based on the fact that he or she says "we're open," and the use of "we" suggests that he or she is involved in the operation.

5 If you brought your own sandwich for a day of skiing but wanted a hot drink, where would you probably get the drink and where would you probably eat?

You would probably go to the Snackpack for your drink and eat in the Time Out Lounge.

Name _____

Read the selection. Then answer the questions that follow.

The Biggest Snowfalls

Imagine your house buried under many feet of snow. Imagine being stuck indoors	13
during a snowstorm that lasted for five or six days. Well, people in the times and	29
places on the chart below experienced just that. These are the greatest snowfalls	42
recorded from the last century up to the year 2000 in the United States. These data	58
were collected by the U.S. Army Corps of Engineers. Do you feel cold just reading	73
the chart, or does it make you wish you could bundle up, go outside, and throw	89
some snowballs?	91
In addition, it's interesting to note, that the lowest temperature on record in	104
the United States, 79.8 degrees below zero Fahrenheit, was observed at Prospect	116
Creek Camp in northern Alaska on January 23, 1971. The lowest in the continental	130
United States was in Rogers Pass, Montana, on January 20, 1954, at -69.7 degrees	144
Fahrenheit. Imagine a record snowfall and record low temperatures almost on the	156
same day!	158

Duration	Place	Date	Inches of Snow
1 month	Tamarack, California	Jan. 1911	390
1 day	Silver Lake, Colorado	Apr. 14–15, 1921	76
1 day	Thompson Pass, Alaska	Dec. 29, 1955	62
1 storm	Mt. Shasta, California	Feb. 13–19, 1959	189
1 storm	Thompson Pass, Alaska	Dec. 26–31, 1955	175
1 season	Mount Baker, Washington	1998–1999	1,140
1 season	Thompson Pass, Alaska	1952–1953	976

© Pearson Education 6

Turn the page.

Answer the questions below.

1 This chart would be helpful if you were researching

A the history of the U.S. Army Corps of Engineers.

Ⓑ extreme weather in the United States.

C why snowflakes are each unique.

D the best sleeping bag for winter camping.

2 The greatest snowfall in a twenty-four-hour period was in

F Tamarack, California, in 1911.

G Mt. Shasta, California, in 1959.

Ⓗ Silver Lake, Colorado, in 1921.

J Thompson Pass, Alaska, in 1955.

3 The data in this chart lead a reader to conclude that

A the Army Corps of Engineers monitors all types of weather.

B more snow falls in the east than in the west.

C the biggest snowfalls happened in the 1930s.

Ⓓ Alaska gets more snow than other states.

4 Based on information in the selection and in the chart, what two things can you say about Montana in winter?

Answers may vary. Possible response: Montana appears to get very cold but does not appear to have any record snowfalls.

Read the selection. Then answer the questions that follow.

Oil: From Under the Ocean to Your Home

The American narrator of *The Cay*, by Theodore Taylor, is a boy named Philip	14
Enright. He lives on a Caribbean island where his father works for the oil industry.	29
A thick dark liquid, oil comes from deep inside the Earth. It is often called "black	45
gold" because it is so valuable to humans. In fact, much of our century's history can	61
be traced to oil fields around the world and the countries that control them.	75

From the crude oil pumped from underground, people manufacture many modern	86
items, including plastics, tires, ink, and paint. Most importantly, from oil we make	99
all the fuels that power our modern world. Gasoline, kerosene, and diesel and jet	113
fuel are all made from oil. North America has about 15 percent of the world's oil,	129
but we use more oil than the other continents combined. The largest reserves are in	144
Asia, especially the countries of the Middle East, which hold about 75 percent of	158
the world's oil.	161

As you read *The Cay*, you'll learn about this industry in the Carribean in the	176
1940s and its role in World War Two. You'll understand that drilling for oil was	191
then, and is still today, a highly skilled and often dangerous job involving hundreds	205
of employees and dozens of steps. The chart below shows the process of getting oil	220
from an underground field to a tanker ship, then to a refinery, and finally to a	236
home or school like yours.	241

Is your home or school heated with an oil product? If so, research the cost	256
per gallon this month and how that compares with the price one year ago. Then	271
compare that with the price of oil in 1944, the year in which *The Cay* is set.	289
You'll likely be surprised!	292

ocean / land
Oil Field → **Oil Well** → **Tanker**

↓

Truck ← **Tanker** ← **Refinery**

Turn the page.

© Pearson Education 6

Answer the questions below.

1 This selection contains a

   A line graph.

   B map.

   C flowchart. *(circled)*

   D schedule.

2 The graphic makes it clear that

   F tanker ships are part of two stages of oil refining. *(circled)*

   G trucks are the first stage in oil refining.

   H most oil is pumped on land.

   J refineries are the final stage.

3 This selection might best have been used

   A to introduce or accompany *The Cay*. *(circled)*

   B as a chapter in *The Cay*.

   C as an article by the main character of *The Cay*.

   D to persuade readers to buy *The Cay*.

4 The graphic about refining suggests that

   F refining oil is an easy task.

   G crude oil refining takes place out in the ocean.

   H refining crude oil may pollute the air. *(circled)*

   J oil refineries are small businesses.

5 The content of *The Cay* includes a lot of history and information about the oil industry. Why is the writer's choice of narrator unusual for this type of book?

Answers may vary. Possible response: A young boy would not be expected to know so much about the oil refining industry.

Read the selection. Then answer the questions that follow.

A New Kind Of Leadership
by Linda Silver, Staff Reporter

Next year, our school is facing some big changes in its organization. For the | 14

past three years, it was led by a committee of parents and teachers. Beginning next | 29

year, a principal will be hired by the committee to provide leadership and authority | 43

while he works with a cooperative team. The principal will be a new addition to | 58

the school, and most teachers and support staff agree that the time for this kind of | 74

change has come. | 77

The chart below shows how this cooperative team will work. The principal will | 90

be chosen and hired by the committee of parents, teachers, and students. Working | 103

closely with the principal will be a team of three people who represent groups of | 118

employees within our school. The chart below shows that in the next year our | 132

school will employ sixteen people to work in new and various roles. | 144

This committee hopes students won't notice much of a difference in the way | 157

things are run, except that they might run more smoothly with only one person in | 172

this leadership role. One person can make a decision more quickly than a whole | 186

committee. Therefore, things might take place more quickly. | 194

Kathy Kovitch, middle grade teacher, says, "It's a very exciting change, and | 206

both students and teachers will be invited to participate in the process of choosing | 220

a principal. It's a chance for us all to think about and discuss what we want in a | 238

leader." | 239

Paul Chin, a parent and committee | 245

member, says that they hope to make a | 253

choice by June. He also hopes that one | 261

or two students will actively participate | 267

in the search process. He also says that | 275

the committee will continue to exist | 281

but that it will focus on fundraising and | 289

long-term planning rather than on the | 295

day-to-day running of the school. | 300

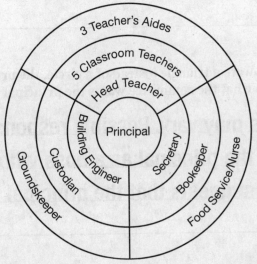

Proposal for Cooperative Team

Turn the page.

- -

Answer the questions below.

1 The organizational chart shows that
  A teachers are more important than secretaries.
  B the custodian is not part of the school staff.
  C the staff is disorganized and needs help.
  (D) the principal is the center of the school staff.

2 The chart suggests that
  F teachers must also help with bookkeeping.
  (G) each employee has a specific and clear role.
  H everyone shares all responsibilities.
  J there are too many teachers in this school.

3 Based on the information in the selection, what conclusion can you draw about the school under its new leadership?
  A The school will have more fundraisers under new leadership.
  (B) The school will be managed better under new leadership.
  C The school will have more guest speakers under new leadership.
  D The school will have better attendance under new leadership.

4 Based on the chart and the information in the selection, what three positions will directly work with the principal, and how will that affect the others in the team?

The head teacher, building engineer, and secretary will carry out the decisions made by the principal and will communicate these decisions to the other members of the team.

5 If the chart were a triangle instead of a circle, the principal would be at the top. How would that change what the committee wants the principal to represent?

Answers may vary. Possible responses: A triangle would present the principal as a boss who tells everyone what to do. A circle suggests that the principal is as much a resource as a boss.

Read the selection. Then answer the questions that follow.

January 8

You might not believe me, but my voice is a river, and I'm not kidding. I'm not | 17

making up some kind of stupid metaphor. I just know I'm going to be a singer or an | 35

actress when I grow up. | 40

Most of the time, my voice just flows along, kind of lazy, a little muddy, and no | 57

one notices it much, including me. Sometimes after a rain, it gurgles over rocks and | 72

splashes with laughter. Sometimes it bends around curves and bubbles over trees | 84

that have fallen into it. Sometimes after an angry storm, it roars, all white-capped, | 98

dangerous, wild, loud, and ferocious. Sometimes it sings and hums, echoing | 109

buzzing insects, cawing crows, or noisy nuthatches. Sometimes it falls suddenly— | 120

but it always recovers, pooling up some in the process. Sometimes it is still, quiet, | 135

and hardly moving at all. Sometimes it is a mirror. Sometimes it is only breath, just | 151

a ripple here and there as blue and green dragonflies alight on its surface. | 165

Turn the page.

Answer the questions below.

1 In this selection, the speaker compares her voice with
   A a fallen tree.
   B a metaphor.
   C a dragonfly.
   (D) moving water.

2 The speaker compares laughter to
   F a mirror of the sky.
   (G) a river after rain.
   H an angry storm.
   J buzzing insects.

3 The speaker is most likely
   (A) a young person with dreams.
   B a scientist who studies rivers.
   C a famous singer with a band.
   D a lonely person who watches birds.

4 How do you know that the speaker probably does not think all metaphors are stupid?

The speaker uses metaphors to describe her voice throughout the selection and to present her voice in a positive light.

Read the selection. Then answer the questions that follow.

Insecurity

It was a cinch, everyone said, nothing to worry about. Miguel's father would put   14

him on a jet in Los Angeles, and his aunt would pick him up in Seattle so he could   33

spend a whole week with his cousins. When his older brother teased him, "You'll   47

never make it past security, shrimp," Miguel tried to ignore the words.   59

The day of his flight, Miguel and his father drove to the airport and hugged   74

good-by, and Miguel entered the line to go through security. After he emptied   87

his pockets, took off his jacket and sneakers, and put them all in the plastic bin,   103

a conveyor belt carried the bin to the X-ray machine. While Miguel waited for a   118

tall, thin man to wave him through the metal detector, his brother's teasing was a   133

mosquito in his ear.   137

As he strolled through, the alarm startled Miguel, and the thin man made   150

him retreat and try again. Again, the alarm sliced the air like a knife, and all the   167

bystanders stopped their conversations and stared. "Over here, please, sir," the thin   179

man waved, frowning, pointing to a bench where a bearded man stood. Miguel   192

watched as a stocky woman waved a wand around the man's forehead and waist.   206

When it was Miguel's turn, he spread his arms and legs like he was in the middle   223

of a jumping jack, and when the wand scanned his chest, it buzzed. "Please empty   238

your pocket, sir," the stocky woman demanded, pointing to Miguel's shirt. Too late,   251

Miguel recalled slipping his professional metal whistle into his shirt pocket, in case   264

his cousins wanted him to referee their soccer game. As he pulled it out, it dangled   280

on its chain.   283

"Nice whistle," she observed, smiling, unlike the thin man. "I'll have to pass it   297

around the X-ray machine."   301

"No problem," Miguel answered, "as long as I can board my plane."   313

"Let's try again," she said, pointing him back to the metal detector. This time,   327

Miguel passed through silently, breathing a deep sigh of relief.   337

Turn the page.

Answer the questions below.

1 The author of this story compared the alarm to

 (A) a knife.

 B a soccer ball.

 C a whistle.

 D Miguel's brother.

2 The thin man and the stocky woman were both

 F Miguel's friends.

 G Miguel's relatives.

 (H) security officers.

 J television actors.

3 Which phrase does not suggest a comparison in the story?

 A like he was in the middle

 (B) pointing to a bench

 C unlike the thin man

 D This time

4 The details of the story suggest that

 F Miguel is shy around his cousins.

 G Miguel's mother lives in Seattle.

 H Miguel flies to Seattle every week.

 (J) Miguel has never flown before.

5 Explain the meaning of the metaphor: "His brother's teasing was a mosquito in his ear."

Miguel's brother annoyed him by teasing him. Miguel felt insecure and couldn't seem to get the words out of his head. His brother was like a pesky insect, and the teasing words were the buzzes in his ear.

Read the selection. Then answer the questions that follow.

Advertising Proposal

October 12, 2004	3
Dear Business Club Members,	7
As you know, our school store, Lem's Locker, is run by the Business Club as	22
a nonprofit corporation. Now in its thirteenth year, Lem's sells school supplies,	34
healthy snacks, and school clothing. Eighty percent of the sales are to students and	48
twenty percent to their parents.	53
This year, the staff of Lem's has an advertising budget of $200. These four	67
proposals are currently on the table:	73

1. *Place mats in local restaurants.* We can buy a 2" by 4" advertisement printed · · · · 88
on 300,000 paper place mats that will be distributed among four popular · · · · 100
restaurants: The Great Wall, Boomers Café, Millie's Diner, and South of · · · · 111
the Border. The printer says it takes about one year for the restaurants to go · · · · 126
through this many place mats. Twenty ads form a border, printed in red or · · · · 140
green on white. Cost: $200. · · · · 145

2. *Advertisements in local movie theaters.* We could use the school's video · · · · 157
studio to produce a thirty-second commercial. Cost to produce: $50. Cost · · · · 168
to run: $100 per month. The theater advertisement agency estimates seven · · · · 179
hundred people would see our ad per week and that over half of these are · · · · 194
students. · · · · 195

3. *Signs at the town playing fields.* These professionally painted metal signs are · · · · 208
guaranteed for fifty years. Cost: $140 each. · · · · 215

4. *Postcards with discount coupons.* Mailing a postcard to every household in · · · · 227
our school would give people something to hang on their refrigerators. In- · · · · 239
house printing cost for six hundred cards: $60; Postage: $180. · · · · 249

We should continue to brainstorm new ideas. I propose that we vote on these · · · · 263
proposals at the next meeting, March 14 at 3 P.M. in the auditorium. I hope to · · · · 279
see you there. Until then, support our school store whenever you can by making · · · · 293
purchases and volunteering to work. Thank you. · · · · 300

Yours in business, · · · · 303

Tamara Douglass, President · · · · 306

Turn the page.

Answer the questions below.

1 Which form of advertising is the least expensive?

(A) place mats in local restaurants

B three months of movie theater ads

C three signs at the town fields

D printing and mailing six hundred postcards

2 Which form of advertising would last the longest?

F place mats

G movie theater ads

(H) signs at playing fields

J postcards with coupons

3 Which sentence expresses a contrast?

A Both the postcards and the place mats could use the same design.

B The place mats and the postcards appeal to parents.

C I think the movie theater ads cost too much.

(D) The signs are outdoors, but the place mats are indoors.

4 Based on the Business Club's budget, how many of the proposals can they act on? Explain your answer.

They can only act on one proposal because acting on more than one would cost more than they have budgeted.

5 If the Business Club wishes to increase the percentage of sales to parents, which two proposals seem most promising?

Postcards and place mats seem most likely to be seen by parents.

Read the selection. Then answer the questions that follow.

Stool Pigeons

Have you ever heard of someone being called a "stool pigeon"? This phrase | 13

refers to someone who tattles or reports on someone else's wrongdoings. If one of | 27

a team of bank robbers goes to the police to tell on all of them, the rest of the team | 47

of robbers might consider that person a rat. If the rat participated in the robbery in | 63

order to get evidence and report it, that person is a stool pigeon. | 76

Where did this figure of speech come from? In the 1700s, North American | 89

hunters searched for pigeons as targets. First, they caught one live bird and tied it | 104

to a stump that looked like a seat or stool. As the bird flapped its wings, it would | 122

attract other pigeons, giving the hunters more targets. The live bird was a trick. | 136

Later, in the language of the 1800s, a "stool pigeon" or "stoolie" began to refer to | 152

someone who lured lawbreakers into his or her trust, and then reported them to the | 167

law. | 168

© Pearson Education 6

Answer the questions below.

1 In this selection, the author

   A informs readers about pigeons.

   B persuades readers to try hunting.

   C explains a figure of speech. *(circled)*

   D wishes to become a stool pigeon.

2 The author of this passage is most likely someone who

   F works in law enforcement.

   G likes knowing the origins of words. *(circled)*

   H teaches college English.

   J has broken the law.

3 This selection suggests that figures of speech

   A only last a few years.

   B can be hundreds of years old. *(circled)*

   C are always about birds.

   D don't make much logical sense.

4 What do the terms "dog-eared" and "hog wild" appear to have in common with the term "stool pigeon"?

All the terms refer to animal behavior and have come to have a new meaning.

Read the selection. Then answer the questions that follow.

The Case of the Missing Calculator

Mr. Feeny has taught math at Cook County Middle School for over twenty years.	14
He loves his students, his textbooks, his classroom, and his computer. He loves the	28
posters on his walls and the windows that overlook the soccer fields behind the	42
school. But most of all, he loves his new calculators.	52
Last summer, Mr. Feeny convinced the Math Department to purchase twenty	63
QV-160s, the most powerful student calculators on the market. They came in a	76
locked suitcase designed to hold a class set. Each calculator was numbered in	89
permanent white ink, from one to twenty. At the beginning of every class, Mr. Feeny	104
unlocks the suitcase and distributes the calculators. He does this six times a day,	118
with six different groups of students. At the end of every class, he checks to make	134
sure they are all in order in their cozy little slots. At the end of every class, they are	153
always accounted for.	156
Except for today: calculator #14 is missing. Mr. Feeny searches the classroom,	168
but it's not here. He opens his six desk drawers, but there is no calculator. He	184
looks through the bookcase—no calculator. He begins to think about his last class,	198
focusing on his movements.	202
Mr. Feeney remembers handing out the calculators to his class. He had walked	215
around the classroom using his own QV-160 to check students' work. He had left	229
the room for a moment to speak with another teacher, Mrs. Patel.	241
Later, he asked her whether she had seen anything that might explain what had	255
happened. As he told his story, she began to smile. "Are you sure you didn't switch	271
your own calculator with #14?" she asked. "My own is right here," Mr. Feeny said,	286
and removed it from his right hand coat pocket. "And in your other pocket?" she	301
asked.	302
There, in the pocket, is #14.	308

Turn the page.

© Pearson Education 6

Answer the questions below.

1 The author of this story means to

   A express that students are untrustworthy.

   B explain why expensive equipment should be locked up.

   C persuade readers to buy a QV-160.

   (D) entertain readers with a surprise ending.

2 The story makes it clear that Mr. Feeny

   (F) placed #14 in his own pocket.

   G cannot trust all his students.

   H should no longer be teaching math.

   J should buy more than twenty calculators.

3 The details in the second paragraph lead us to conclude that

   A the QV-160 is overrated.

   B only a few students use the QV-160s.

   C many calculators have been stolen from the school.

   (D) Mr. Feeny is very careful with the calculators.

4 The last sentence suggests that

   F Mr. Feeny would never find the missing calculator.

   G Ben probably took the calculator.

   H Ben hadn't left for the day.

   (J) Mr. Feeny will feel foolish.

5 The teacher might have learned a lesson in this story. What lesson about drawing conclusions does "The Case of the Missing Calculator" illustrate?

The lesson the story teaches is that anyone can make a mistake, and that others can help us solve problems.

Read the selection. Then answer the questions that follow.

No More Dragons

Back in the days when everything was new, there existed a dragon, a gigantic	14
flying creature with green scales, wide wings, and a long, powerful tail. Dragon was	28
surely handsome and strong, but he was also a bully who teased the other animals.	43
Dragon often picked arguments, especially with creatures smaller than himself, and,	54
of course, he always won. He even gobbled fireflies when he wasn't all that hungry.	69
The other animals begged him to stop, but Dragon would not heed their warnings.	83
"He's very scary," observed Skunk. "And very dangerous," accused Deer.	93
One summer, Dragon ate so many fireflies, he began to breathe flames. Whenever	106
he felt aggressive, he could shoot fire at any target he chose. "You've got to be	122
careful!" the animals cried. "When the Creator sees what you have done, you will	136
be in trouble!" But Dragon didn't listen; he laughed.	145
One September night while Dragon slept, he snored and the entire forest burst	158
into flames! As oak trees burned into black spikes, Eagle and Owl flew many	172
kilometers away, and Trout and Pike took refuge on the river bottom. The empty	186
forest reeked of smoke, and countless animals lost their homes. For this, the Creator	200
punished Dragon with the following decree: "From this day forward, Dragon, you	212
will no longer be gigantic and strong, but tiny and weak. You will not soar among	228
the clouds but buzz along the river's surface, as low as a creature can fly. Your	244
wings will no longer be thick and muscular, but paper-thin and delicate. Your body	258
will not be powerful and green but slender and black, and from now on, your name	274
will be *dragonfly*."	277
So if you spot a dragonfly flitting across the surface of a pond, recall Dragon and	293
his arrogant mistake. Be gentle with the forest and your friends, or a similar fate	308
could befall you.	311

© Pearson Education 6

Turn the page.

Answer the questions below.

1 You can tell from the first paragraph that you are reading

    A a newspaper article.

    B a letter.

    C an autobiography.

    (D) a legend.

2 When Dragon laughed at the end of the second paragraph, it means that

    (F) he didn't care what the others said.

    G his throat was tickled by the fireflies.

    H he thought the Creator was very funny.

    J he thought everyone was joking.

3 The Creator in this story appears to be a

    A bird.

    (B) judge.

    C dragon.

    D bully.

4 In the last paragraph, the author explicitly writes about the story's lesson or moral. Do you think the author exaggerates here or means what he or she says literally?

Answers may vary. Possible response: I think the author exaggerates here because I do not believe I might be turned into an insect.

5 After reading this story, one student concluded, "This punishment is too harsh. The Creator could have taught Dragon a lesson without. . . ." Identify what aspect of the Creator's lesson might have seemed too harsh and explain how the punishment could have been milder.

Answers may vary. Possible response: The Creator could have punished the Dragon without changing him so dramatically. The Creator could have made him smaller but not incredibly small, or just taken away his fire-breathing ability.

© Pearson Education 6

174

Read the selection. Then answer the questions that follow.

What Do Teenagers Eat?

To find out what teenagers at our middle school eat, I took a survey of one | 16

hundred of our students, ages twelve to fifteen, during the week of April 14. I asked | 32

them to rate how often they eat certain kinds of foods. A chart showing the raw data | 49

is shown below. | 52

When asked how often they eat fresh fruits, vegetables, and salads, 17 percent | 65

replied "never." About two-thirds of us eat these sometimes and only 20 percent of | 79

us eat them daily. | 83

Every one of us eats pizza and chips. They are the universal teenage foods. A | 98

dozen of us admit to eating pizza every day! | 107

There were a few surprises. For example, three out of every four students drink | 121

bottled water every day. Also, over a third of us eat candy every day. Only 15 | 137

percent of us don't eat meat, and a third of us never eat fish. Over half of us drink | 156

soda every day. | 159

You can draw your own conclusions, but I think this survey shows that most | 173

students at Middleton Middle School need to improve their diets! | 183

	Never	Sometimes	Daily
Fresh fruit, vegetables, salad	17	63	20
Cereal	32	51	17
Chips	0	79	21
Pizza	0	88	12
Candy	3	58	39
Chicken or beef	15	70	15
Fish	33	62	5
Sugary desserts	2	53	45
Soda	3	37	60
Bottled water	1	24	75
Milk	24	44	32

© Pearson Education 6

Turn the page.

Answer the questions below.

1 The students at this school
- **(A)** eat more pizza than salad.
- **B** eat fish every day.
- **C** never eat sugary desserts.
- **D** drink more milk than bottled water.

2 Which of these is a valid generalization?
- **F** Most students never drink milk.
- **(G)** Most students eat fruits or vegetables sometimes.
- **H** Many middle school students don't eat meat.
- **J** Cereal is a popular breakfast among middle school students.

3 Which of these is an invalid generalization about the teenagers surveyed?
- **A** Everyone eats pizza and chips.
- **(B)** All students occasionally eat sugary desserts.
- **C** Nearly everyone drinks bottled water.
- **D** None of the vegetarians eat pizza or chips.

4 What, after pizza and chips, appears to be a nearly "universal" teenage favorite? Explain your answer.

Soda appears to be a nearly universal teenage favorite. Over half the teenagers surveyed, drink it every day.

© Pearson Education 6

Read the selection. Then answer the questions that follow.

Chapter Two

My mom and dad were married at the town landfill, and yes, I am certain of this	17
because I've seen the photographs. Dad ran the Transfer Station (as they called it	31
officially) in Bethel, Ohio, and Mom took a part-time job there on Saturdays and	45
Sundays. Well, Dad started showing up on Saturdays and Sundays even though	57
he wasn't scheduled, and the next thing you know they were having dinner on	71
Saturday evenings and again on Sundays. After a year, they decided that the	84
Transfer Station would run a lot more smoothly if they returned to their regular	98
hours, which meant that they ought to get married so they wouldn't have to rely on	114
the landfill to see each other.	120
So when it came time to organize the wedding, the landfill seemed the logical	134
site. They spread carpets all around and built a fancy wooden canopy in the	148
unloading zone. Some three hundred wedding guests cheered as the limousine	159
pulled up to the recycling bins and they tiptoed out, Dad in a tuxedo and top hat and	177
Mom in a full-length, white wedding gown. Someone spread rose petals in front of	191
my mother as she walked to the canopy where the town clerk waited. As the happy	207
couple recited vows of everlasting love, several of my dad's friends attached the	220
longest, loudest chain of clatter behind the limousine with a sign that said "Just	234
Married: Don't 'Dump' Me Yet!" As they drove away to the inn for the reception,	249
my mother's brother Jared sang a tune he'd written especially for the occasion	262
called "Recycled Love."	265
"Sure, it was a funny place for a wedding," my mother recalls today, "but it was	281
also unique. Our marriage was one of a kind . . . right from the start." I swear I	300
laugh every time I stare at those photographs.	308

© Pearson Education 6

Turn the page.

- -

Answer the questions below.

1 What did the writer's parents have in common as the story begins?

   A love of roses

   (B) working at the Transfer Station

   C wanting to get married

   D desire to ride in a limousine

2 The story shows that the speaker's parents were

   (F) willing to do something unusual.

   G extremely traditional.

   H sentimental about how they met.

   J unhappy with their jobs.

3 Which of the following features of the speaker's parents' wedding is probably not typical of most weddings?

   A the canopy

   B the attire

   (C) the setting

   D the photos

4 The "voice" of this memoir is

   (F) casual and friendly, like a story with a voice.

   G formal to the point of being stuffy.

   H written like a newspaper article.

   J very emotional because of the content.

5 Does the speaker find his or her parents' wedding photos more amusing or embarrassing? Explain your answer.

The author finds his or her parents' wedding more amusing than embarrassing because he or she laughs whenever he or she looks at the pictures and seems to have looked at them and asked about them more than a few times.

Read the selection. Then answer the questions that follow.

The Sea Lamprey: A Nervous System Model

The sea lamprey is a fascinating animal that lives in water. It is born in rivers	16
that flow to the sea in many parts of northeastern North America. At the end of its	33
"adolescence," the lamprey transforms into an adult and heads to the ocean to live	47
out its adult life.	51
Lampreys look like eels. Unlike eels, they have no bones, though their bodies	64
do contain a spinal cord. Lampreys spend their first seven years burrowed in the	78
sand in freshwater streams. Blind during this stage of life, they feed on nutrients in	93
the water and breathe through gills. At the time of their transformation, lampreys	106
grow eyes and sucker mouths, and their limber bodies turn from brown to black and	121
silver. They also grow from six to twelve inches to as much as three feet after they	138
complete their adult journey out to sea.	145
Biologists, especially the ones who study how nerves function during injury and	157
healing, are interested in lampreys. Some of these biologists discovered that if you	170
cut a young lamprey's spinal cord, the nerves will grow back together again. The	184
healed animal can swim just as well as it did before its spinal cord was cut! Curious	201
to know more about this amazing ability, biologists catch lampreys and use them to	215
study nerve regeneration, the ability of a nerve to grow back after it has been cut.	231
Thanks to the secrets this unusual creature offers and the scientists who study	244
them, nerve damage in human spinal cords may one day be able to be repaired.	259

© Pearson Education 6

Turn the page.

Answer the questions below.

1 How do adult lampreys differ from young ones?

    A They have a spinal cord.

    B They live in fresh water.

    C They are brown.

    (D) They have eyes.

2 Which of these is a valid generalization?

    F Some biologists spend seven years studying one stream.

    G When the human spinal cord is cut, it grows back.

    (H) When animals transform, they change physically.

    J Most scientists who study lampreys also study eels.

3 Which of these is a faulty generalization?

    A Lampreys may shed light on nerve regeneration.

    B Underwater, eels are often mistaken for lampreys.

    C Vertebrates are animals with backbones.

    (D) All eels lack a spinal cord but have bones.

4 Is the following generalization valid or faulty? Give your reasons.

    A cure for most types of human spinal cord injury will come from the study of lampreys.

This is a faulty generalization. Even if scientists can discover how and why the lamprey's spinal cord heals itself and apply that to cure human injuries, it is unclear whether such a cure will work for "most" types of human spinal cord injuries.

5 When the lamprey transforms, two of its general needs must change, otherwise it would not leave the river or stream or grow so much in length. Generalize from those two details what two basic needs of the lamprey must change as a result of its transformation.

As a result of its transformation, the lamprey needs a saltwater environment and food that is not available or not available in sufficient quantity in the freshwater environment.